29.295

THEORY OF PROBABILITY

THEORY
OF
PROBABILITY

M. E. MUNROE
Assistant Professor of Mathematics
University of Illinois

New York   Toronto   London
McGRAW-HILL BOOK COMPANY, INC.
1951

THEORY OF PROBABILITY

II

THE MAPLE PRESS COMPANY, YORK, PA.

PREFACE

This book is the outgrowth of an undergraduate-graduate course that the author has offered for the past few years at the University of Illinois.

The modern theory of probability is based on the Lebesgue-Stieltjes integral and so requires a rather extensive background in analysis for a rigorous presentation. However, a formal development of this theory should be intelligible to students with considerably less preparation, and this book is intended to be just such a formal summary. We have attempted to keep the analytical level of the book down to the point where one year of calculus can serve as a prerequisite for the course. On the other hand, we have not hesitated to include important theorems that cannot be proved on this level. We have tried to be honest with the student by pointing out the lapses in rigor that necessarily occur because of the nature of our undertaking.

The true flavor of modern probability theory is best seen in the limit theorems; therefore Chapters 2 to 6 have been designed primarily as an introduction to Chapters 8 to 11. Stochastic variables are introduced almost simultaneously with the notion of mathematical probability, and the discrete and continuous cases are treated side by side throughout. This is an unorthodox arrangement for an elementary text, but it seems desirable in view of our aim to push beyond the problem course in permutations and combinations that is often regarded as an introduction to probability theory.

A large portion of the material in this book can be found, in slightly different form, in Cramér's *Mathematical Methods of Statistics* and in Uspensky's *Introduction to Mathematical Probability*. The author takes this opportunity to acknowledge his indebtedness to these sources.

Professor J. L. Doob has been very kind in undertaking to criticize the manuscript in various stages of preparation. His suggestions have strengthened the work immeasurably.

M. E. MUNROE

URBANA, ILL.
November, 1950

v

CONTENTS

vii

CHAPTER 1

PERMUTATIONS AND COMBINATIONS

This chapter contains only a very brief summary of the subject of permutations and combinations. It is designed as a review rather than as an introduction to the subject. For the student who finds this chapter inadequate, we have listed at the end several references in which he will find a much fuller treatment. In addition to these references, we should also recommend to the student the book from which he studied college algebra.

We take up permutations and combinations, not because these topics form an integral part of the theory of probability, but because they are useful tools in solving many problems that illustrate the fundamental ideas of probability theory. The emphasis in later chapters will be on these fundamental ideas, and the problems assigned there are designed to help the student understand these ideas. But if a specific example is to be of any help to the student in understanding a general principle, he must be able to work the example without wasting all his energy on mechanical details. The student who is weak in arithmetic will have trouble with principles of accounting; the one who is weak in French grammar will get lost trying to study French literature. Similarly, the main body of this course is apt to elude the student who neglects the more or less mechanical aids such as those found in this chapter.

1. Formulas for ^nP_r and ^nC_r

Suppose there are n objects, distinguishable one from the other in some way. If r of these n objects are laid out in some order, we say that this procedure describes a *permutation* of the r objects. If we count all the different permutations thus obtainable from the entire set of n objects (permutations being considered different if they are described by different sets of r objects or if they are described by different methods of ordering the same r objects), we refer to the result as the "number of permutations of n things r at a time" and denote it by the symbol ^nP_r.

The formula for ^nP_r in terms of n and r may be obtained by the fol-

1

lowing device: Let us think of a permutation as described by taking a box with r compartments (numbered from 1 to r) and filling it by placing one of the n objects in each compartment. Now, there are obviously n different ways of filling the first compartment. For each of these n ways, there are $n - 1$ ways of filling the second compartment. Hence, there are $n(n - 1)$ different ways (different in the sense that they will lead to different permutations) of filling the first two compartments. Continuing in this manner, we arrive at the familiar formula:

$$^nP_r = n(n - 1)(n - 2) \cdots (n - r + 1).$$

A neater way of expressing this formula is obtained by means of a device the student should learn to use. The expression for ^nP_r is very similar to $n!$. The only trouble is that the first $n - r$ factors are missing. If we interpret "missing" to mean they have been divided out, we have

(1) $$^nP_r = \frac{n!}{(n - r)!}.$$

We describe a *combination* of n things r at a time by choosing a set of r objects from the parent set of n objects and disregarding the order (if any) of those chosen. Thus, for every combination of n things r at a time there are $^rP_r = r!$ permutations. Hence, the number of permutations is $r!$ times the number of combinations. In symbols:

$$^nP_r = r! \, ^nC_r.$$

So, we divide (1) by $r!$ and obtain the formula for the number of combinations of n things r at a time:

(2) $$^nC_r = \frac{n!}{r! \, (n - r)!}.$$

The combination numbers ^nC_r appear in many different connections in mathematics, and unfortunately there is no universally accepted symbol for them. We shall stick to the symbol ^nC_r. Others in common use are C^n_r, $\binom{n}{r}$, $_nC_r$, $C(n,r)$ and $C_{n,r}$. Uspensky's *Introduction to Mathematical Probability*, which we recommend again and again as collateral reading, has the r and n reversed. The thing we call ^nC_r Uspensky writes C^r_n. Because of this wide diversity of notation, the student would do well to check carefully on the author's convention in each new work he reads.

An interesting arrangement of the numbers ^nC_r is given by Pascal's triangle:

$$
\begin{array}{ccccccccccccccc}
&&&&&&& 1 \\
&&&&&& 1 && 1 \\
&&&&& 1 && 2 && 1 \\
&&&& 1 && 3 && 3 && 1 \\
&&& 1 && 4 && 6 && 4 && 1 \\
&& 1 && 5 && 10 && 10 && 5 && 1 \\
& 1 && 6 && 15 && 20 && 15 && 6 && 1 \\
1 && 7 && 21 && 35 && 35 && 21 && 7 && 1 \\
&&&&&& \cdots
\end{array}
$$

Successive rows represent successive values of n, and in each row the entries read from left to right are the values of ^nC_r given by successive values of r. We have listed above the entries for $n = 0, 1, 2, \ldots, 7$. An interesting feature of the Pascal triangle is that each entry is the sum of the two above it (see Prob. 18 at the end of this chapter). In many cases this rule furnishes an easy way of computing combination numbers.

The student will notice that each row of the triangle begins with an entry corresponding to $r = 0$. Furthermore, for each n, we have set $^nC_0 = 1$. This is quite consistent with the formula. If we note that $(n - 1)! = n!/n$, then it seems reasonable to say that $0! = 1!/1 = 1$; and (2) yields

$$^nC_0 = \frac{n!}{0!n!} = 1.$$

The inclusion of $^nC_0$ obviously makes for symmetry in Pascal's triangle, but we might question its significance in terms of combinations. It counts the so-called *vacuous combination*—the process of making a pass at the set of n objects, but not taking any. In some problems we shall want to count this possibility; in others we shall want to exclude it.

The student must learn to distinguish between combinations and permutations. The distinction lies in whether or not the order of objects chosen is to be considered. For example, there are 24 permutations of the numbers 1, 2, 3, 4 taken three at a time:

123	124	134	234
132	142	143	243
213	214	314	324
231	241	341	342
312	412	413	423
321	421	431	432

However, there are only 4 combinations—one indicated by each column above. All entries in a given column are merely rearrangements one of the other, and these do not constitute new combinations. Sometimes textbook problems "In how many ways can so and so be done?" leave room for doubt as to whether combinations or permutations are to be counted. For instance, we have given four answers to Prob. 6 at the end of this chapter. Each represents a different interpretation of the problem. Some of the interpretations are rather artificial, but each is theoretically justifiable, and the student should determine what interpretation is used to arrive at each answer.

To anticipate for a moment, probability will be computed in many simple examples by counting "favorable cases" and "possible cases" and dividing the former by the latter. The cases under consideration will frequently be combinations or permutations, and often we can analyze the problem in either way. In such problems we must take care to count the same thing in both numerator and denominator.

Occasionally, the student will want to use the argument we employed to find ^nP_r. That is, he will reason that, if a first step can be taken in n_1 ways and for each of these a second step can be taken in n_2 ways, then the two steps can be taken in n_1n_2 ways. In general, this type of argument leads to a count of permutations. However, there are exceptions to this rule. The above argument will lead to a count of combinations in case the results of the two steps are not permutable, *i.e.*, in case the two steps are of an essentially different nature so that no combinations are counted twice.

2. Example—Poker Hands

Perhaps an illustrative example will serve to clarify this last remark. Let us find the number of 5-card poker hands of each of the following types:

(*a*) One pair (other 3 different)
(*b*) Two pairs (1 odd card)
(*c*) Three of a kind (2 odd cards)
(*d*) Full house (3 of a kind and a pair)
(*e*) Four of a kind

Here, presumably, we are to count 5-card combinations. At any rate, let us proceed to do that.

(*a*) There are 52 ways of choosing the first card. For each of these there are 3 ways of completing the pair. Now, if we say there are

52×3 ways of getting the pair, we shall be counting every combination twice. For instance, the ace of spades is one of the 52 possibilities for the first card; and the ace of hearts is one of the 3 possibilities that goes with it. However, the ace of hearts is one of the 52 possibilities for the first card; and the ace of spades is one of the 3 that goes with it. Thus, in the 52×3 ways of getting a pair, we have counted (AS,AH) and (AH,AS); but these 2 ways lead to the same pair. The same is true of every other pair; so the number of 2-card combinations containing pairs is $52 \times \frac{3}{2}$. Now, to fill the rest of the hand: For every pair there are 48 ways of getting a third card which is different. For every such choice of the first 3 cards, there are 44 allowable choices for the fourth. Similarly, we are left with 40 choices for the fifth card. Again, straight multiplication yields a count of the permutations of the last 3 cards; so it is necessary to divide by 3!. Now, there arises the following question: There are $52 \times \frac{3}{2}$ two-card combinations which are pairs; for each of these there are $48 \times 44 \times 40/3!$ combinations of 3 odd cards. If we multiply these two numbers together, do we not again count permutations? The answer is no, because these things do not permute. We count no 5-card combinations twice by listing the pair first and the 3 odd cards second. Thus, the answer to part (a) is:

$$\frac{52 \times 3}{2!} \cdot \frac{48 \times 44 \times 40}{3!}.$$

(b) Here we count the pairs in the same way. There are $52 \times \frac{3}{2}$ ways of getting the first pair. For each of these, there are $48 \times \frac{3}{2}$ ways of getting the second pair. But these pairs permute. To multiply these two numbers together and quit would be to count aces and kings and also kings and aces. The result must be divided by 2 again. Finally, for every 2-pair combination there are 44 ways of choosing the odd card. The odd card does not permute with the pairs; so multiplication by 44 yields the total count of 5-card combinations containing 2 pairs. The answer is:

$$\frac{\dfrac{52 \times 3}{2!} \cdot \dfrac{48 \times 3}{2!}}{2!} \cdot 44.$$

These two cases illustrate all the difficulties that arise. We leave the remainder of the example as an exercise for the student.

3. Binomial Coefficients

So much for permutations and combinations as such. Before moving on, we should look at some of the other uses of the combination numbers ^nC_r. Perhaps their most important appearance is in the binomial theorem:

$$(1) \qquad (a + b)^n = \sum_{r=0}^{n} {}^nC_r a^r b^{n-r}.$$

Because of the role they play in this important theorem, the numbers ^nC_r are frequently referred to as *binomial coefficients*. In fact the student will find that this is the name usually given to these numbers.

The binomial formula (1) is an identity in a and b. That is, if a and b are considered as independent variables, the function on the left is equal to the function on the right at every point in the ab plane. Clearly, if each side of such an identity is added to or multiplied by the same quantity, the result is another identity. Furthermore, differentiation with respect to either of the variables yields another identity. (Note that integration may introduce an extraneous constant.)

Since (1)—or any identity derived from it—holds over the entire ab plane, it holds at any given point or along any given curve. Thus, the substitution of specific values for a and b or substitution from an equation relating a and b will yield a correct result. To illustrate the use of these techniques for getting information from (1), let us set $a = b = 1$. The result is

$$(2) \qquad \sum_{r=0}^{n} {}^nC_r = 2^n.$$

This says (among other things) that the number of all combinations of n things (including the vacuous one) is 2^n.

If we take the partial derivative of (1) with respect to a, we have

$$n(a + b)^{n-1} = \sum_{r=0}^{n} r \, {}^nC_r a^{r-1} b^{n-r};$$

Multiply by a:

$$na(a + b)^{n-1} = \sum_{r=0}^{n} r \, {}^nC_r a^r b^{n-r};$$

and consider the special case $a + b = 1$:

$$(3) \qquad \sum_{r=0}^{n} r \, {}^nC_r a^r (1 - a)^{n-r} = na.$$

The significance of this last result we shall see later. The method used to obtain it is one commonly employed in making computations with binomial coefficients.

REFERENCES FOR FURTHER STUDY

Hall and Knight, *Higher Algebra*, London (1936), Chaps. XI, XII, XIII.

Levy and Roth, *Elements of Probability*, Oxford (1936), Chaps. III, VII.

Whitworth, *Choice and Chance*, New York (1927), Chaps. I, II, III.

PROBLEMS

1. How many Greek-letter fraternities can be given distinct names of 3 different letters each? (There are 24 letters in the Greek alphabet.) *Ans.* $^{24}P_3$.

2. The same as Prob. 1, but the letters in a name need not be different. *Ans.* 24^3.

3. How many fraternity names are there with either 2 or 3 letters, all different? with repetitions? *Ans.* $^{24}P_2 + {}^{24}P_3$; $24^2 + 24^3$.

4. In how many ways may a party of 10 people be seated in a row? at a round table? *Ans.* $10!$, $9!$.

5. In how many ways may a party of 5 couples be seated at a round table with men and women alternating? *Ans.* $5! \times 4!$.

6. In how many ways can 52 cards be dealt into 4 hands of 13 cards each? *Ans.* $52!$, $52!/(13!)^4$, $52!/4!$, $52!/4!(13!)^4$.

7. How many different 13-card hands can be obtained from a 52-card deck? *Ans.* $^{52}C_{13}$.

8. How many of these 13-card hands will contain a 7-card suit? *Ans.* $4 \cdot {}^{13}C_7 \cdot {}^{39}C_6$.

9. How many 5-card poker hands contain three of a kind, a full house, four of a kind? (See Sec. 2.) *Ans.* 54,912; 3,744; 624.

10. How many integers less than a billion contain five 7's? *Ans.* $9^4 \cdot {}^9C_5$.

11. How many integers less than a billion consist of 1's and 2's only? *Ans.* $2^{10} - 2$.

12. How many of the integers in Prob. 11 contain three 1's? *Ans.* 210.

13. How many different ordered pairs of numbers can result from the throwing of two dice? *Ans.* 36.

14. How many of the results in Prob. 13 give a total of 7? 11? *Ans.* 6, 2.

15. How many 5-man basketball teams can be chosen from a squad of 12? *Ans.* 792.

16. If the 12-man squad in Prob. 15 consists of 3 centers, 5 forwards, and 4 guards, how many teams (1 center, 2 forwards, 2 guards) can be chosen?   *Ans.*   180.

17. Show that $^nC_r = {^nC_{n-r}}$.

18. Show that $^{n+1}C_r = {^nC_r} + {^nC_{r-1}}$.

19. Use the identity in Prob. 18 to prove the binomial theorem by mathematical induction.

20. Show that

$$\sum_{r=0}^{n} (-1)^r \, {^nC_r} = 0.$$

21. Show that

$$\sum_{r=0}^{n} \frac{1}{r!(n-r)!} = \frac{2^n}{n!}.$$

22. Show that

$$\sum_{r=0}^{n} r^2 \, {^nC_r} a^r (1-a)^{n-r} = na(1-a) + (na)^2.$$

23. Show that, for $0 \leq k \leq n$,

$$\sum_{r=0}^{k} {^nC_r} \, {^nC_{k-r}} = {^{2n}C_k}.$$

Hint: $(1+x)^n(1+x)^n = (1+x)^{2n}$.   Compute the coefficient of x^k on each side of this equation.

24. Show that,

$$\sum_{r=0}^{n} ({^nC_r})^2 = {^{2n}C_n}.$$

25. Show that, for $0 \leq 2k \leq n$,

$$\sum_{r=0}^{2k} (-1)^r \, {^nC_r} \, {^nC_{2k-r}} = (-1)^k \, {^nC_k}.$$

Hint: $(1+x)^n(1-x)^n = (1-x^2)^n$.

26. Show that (except, perhaps, for an additive constant)

$$\sum_{r=0}^{k} {^nC_r} x^{n-r} (1-x)^r = (n-k) \, {^nC_k} \int_{0}^{x} t^{n-k-1}(1-t)^k \, dt.$$

Hint: Differentiate with respect to x.

27. Show that (except, perhaps, for an additive constant)

$$\sum_{r=0}^{k} {}^nC_r x^r (1 - x)^{n-r} = (n - k)\, {}^nC_k \int_x^1 t^k (1 - t)^{n-k-1}\, dt.$$

Note: The constant of integration left unaccounted for in Probs. 26 and 27 is actually zero in each case. See Prob. 12, Chap. 7.

CHAPTER 2

MATHEMATICAL PROBABILITY

To the pure mathematician, probability is merely a function satisfying certain axioms. Later in this chapter we shall give a set of axioms that will serve as a basis for the development of the mathematical discipline known as the "theory of probability." First, however, we should give some attention to the question of the physical significance of probability.

4. An Elementary Definition

Probability might be described as a "measure of likelihood." That is, the probability of a physical event will be a number which describes, in accordance with certain fixed conventions, the likelihood of occurrence of the event.

For any such numerical measurements we have to agree on a scale, and the standard convention is that probabilities range from 0 to 1, with impossible events assigned probability 0 and logically certain events assigned probability 1. Furthermore, we want the intermediate probabilities assigned in such a way that, the more likely an event is, the greater will be its probability.

This last result can be accomplished in many ways, and we might be tempted to be more explicit by saying that we want probability proportional to likelihood. However, likelihood is too abstract a quantity for this to make much sense. We get a more satisfactory picture by considering the frequency of occurrence of an event. Let us say that the probability of an event will be proportional to the frequency with which we should expect the event to occur. Clearly, the factor of proportionality (to give probabilities ranging from 0 to 1) is the total number of opportunities for occurrence of the event. So we might say that the probability of an event is its expected relative frequency.

The student must not confuse what we have called "expected relative frequency" with observed frequencies of occurrence (past, present, or future). The question of the relationship between probability and experimental frequency is one that can be discussed more intelligently at the end of a probability course than at the beginning. We shall return to it in Chap. 11. All we want to point out here is that if there is any convincing reason for expecting a certain event to happen with a certain relative frequency, then it is that relative frequency (not its square, for instance) that we should take as the probability of the given event.

The usual procedure in determining the proper assignment of probabilities to physical events is to begin with the simplest cases, where the proper assignment is obvious, and develop rules and formulas to describe more complicated cases in terms of these simpler ones. Accordingly, we begin with a definition that covers the simplest type of physical situation.

Definition 1.   If an experiment can produce n different results all of which are equally likely and if r of these results are defined as favorable, the probability of a favorable result is r/n.

Now, equally likely results have the same expected relative frequencies. It does not matter whether we regard this as an obvious statement, a definition of equal likelihood, or a definition of expected frequency. The point is that because of this fact (or definition, or what have you) Definition 1 is consistent with the idea that probability be proportional to expected frequency.

While Definition 1 is inadequate as a basis for the development of the mathematical theory of probability, it is essential that we have something of the sort to relate the notion of probability to that of likelihood. The theorems and formulas of mathematical probability theory are best developed from a set of axioms (see Sec. 8), and that is the way we shall proceed. It would be very unsatisfactory, however, to have a purely abstract theory with no relation to physical events at all; and Definition 1 (and its twin brother Definition 3—see Sec. 12) serve as important connecting links between the mathematical theory and the physical world. Furthermore, these physical definitions (wherever they apply) give probability the physical meaning we should like it to have—a measure of likelihood.

We are still faced with the (essentially psychological) problem of determining when events are equally likely. We have suggested equally likely events as the simplest physical situation because they are the easiest to spot with a reasonable degree of assurance. Fundamentally, what we do when we apply Definition 1 is to *assume* the equal likelihood of certain events. We should try to make these assumptions reasonable, but logically they have to stand as assumptions only. There is no way of proving them.

The necessity for making assumptions in order to fit a physical problem to a mathematical formula is not peculiar to the calculus of probabilities. In almost any calculus book one can find the problem, "Find the work done in filling an upright cylindrical tank a feet in radius and h feet in height by pumping water in through an inlet in the bottom." At this point, one blithely writes

$$W = 62.4 \int_0^h \pi a^2 x \, dx.$$

Now no physical tank is a perfect cylinder; the inlet presents an additional irregularity; water is not quite a perfect fluid; etc. However, if we *assume* that none of these irregularities exists, then the mathematical theory of the definite integral guarantees that the above is the correct answer.

Probability is not alone among the branches of mathematics in that assumptions are necessary for its applications to the physical world. Its only claim to fame in this respect is that in probability problems the experts disagree more violently and argue more loudly about the assumptions to be made.

5. Example—Roulette

As an example of the type of situation described in Definition 1, let us study the game of roulette. There are minor variations here and there, but the standard game (at Monte Carlo) is played with a wheel with 37 equally spaced slots, numbered from 0 through 36. In addition to a number, each slot has a color. The zero is green, and the others are either red or black (18 of each). Actually, the colors alternate around the wheel; but the numbers are irregularly placed in such a way that 1, 3, 5, 7, 9, 12, 14, 16, 18, 19, 21, 23, 25, 27, 30, 32, 34, 36 are red and the others are black. The wheel is spun, and a ball is rolled around it. When wheel and ball have slowed down sufficiently, the ball falls into a slot; and bets are then paid off on the basis of the slot into which it falls.

The educational feature of the game from our point of view is the way in which bets may be placed. There is a board on which the numbers are arranged as follows:

$$0$$

$$\underline{1} \qquad 2 \qquad \underline{3}$$

$$4 \qquad \underline{5} \qquad 6$$

$$\underline{7} \qquad 8 \qquad \underline{9}$$

$$10 \qquad 11 \qquad \underline{12}$$

$$13 \qquad \underline{14} \qquad 15$$

$$\underline{16} \qquad 17 \qquad \underline{18}$$

$$\underline{19} \qquad 20 \qquad 21$$

$$22 \qquad \underline{23} \qquad 24$$

$$\underline{25} \qquad 26 \qquad \underline{27}$$

$$28 \qquad 29 \qquad \underline{30}$$

$$31 \qquad \underline{32} \qquad 33$$

$$\underline{34} \qquad 35 \qquad \underline{36}$$

The colors are indicated on the board too. We have done this by underlining the red numbers. Bets are made by placing chips at an appropriate place on the board. One may bet on a single number, any 2 adjacent numbers (either across or down, not diagonally), any square of 4 numbers, a combination of zero with any 1 or with all 3 of the numbers adjacent to it, any row of 3 numbers, any 2 adjacent rows, or any column of 12 numbers. (The zero is not considered as being in the middle column.) In addition to the above number array on which these bets may be indicated, the board provides spaces on which one may indicate bets on the numbers 1 to 18 (passe), 19 to 36 (manque), the even numbers, the odd numbers, the red numbers, the black numbers, and each of the three dozens 1 to 12, 13 to 24, 25 to 36.

It would seem reasonable to assume that the 37 numbers are equally likely (there is no way of proving this mathematically); therefore we may apply Definition 1 to find the probability of winning any particular bet. The point we want to stress here is that the description of the game furnishes us with our situation (37 numbers) and our law of probability ($\frac{1}{37}$ times the number of numbers covered by the bet). The definition of "favorable" (*i.e.*, the particular bet we want to talk about) has nothing to do with this. However, having described the situation and formulated the law of probability, we can immediately compute the probability of winning on any of the bets listed above. The probability of winning on red is $\frac{18}{37}$; on even, $\frac{18}{37}$; on the first column, $12\frac{2}{37}$; on the first two rows, $6\frac{6}{37}$; etc.   There are 155 different bets covered by the discussion we have given; so, with a single description of a situation and a probability law, we solve 155 different problems.   As a matter of fact, from a purely theoretical point of view, we solve a lot more than that.   In Chap. 1 we saw that the total number of combinations of n things, including the vacuous one, is 2^n.   We now exclude the vacuous combination and see that there are $2^{37} - 1 = 137,438,953,471$ different bets imaginable, though only 155 of these are accepted at Monte Carlo.   Clearly, each of these hundred-odd billion problems is solvable immediately from the law of probability we have formulated.

All this is typical of probability problems in general.   The mathematical formulation should lead to a law which gives the probability of every event connected with the given situation.   Usually not all this information will be needed in any given study; nevertheless, it will be available if the problem has been correctly formulated.

6. The Addition Principle

Suppose, in the roulette game, we place two bets on the same spin of the wheel.   Suppose, further, that no number is covered by both bets. For example, we might bet on the first and third columns, not on the first column and the second row.   This latter combination covers the 4 twice.   Under these circumstances, it is easily seen that the probability of winning one or the other of the two bets is equal to the sum of the probabilities of winning each of the two separately.

This addition principle is a property of probabilities in general.   In fact, for situations covered by Definition 1, it is almost obvious.   If E_1 is an event consisting of r_1 results and E_2 is an event consisting of r_2 results from the same experiment and if no one of the n possible results is contained in both events, then the two events together consist of $r_1 + r_2$ results.   So, by Definition 1, the probability of one or the other is

$$\frac{r_1 + r_2}{n} = \frac{r_1}{n} + \frac{r_2}{n};$$

but the right-hand side is the sum of the probabilities of the separate events.

7. Example—Two Dice

Before proceeding to formal mathematical definitions, let us consider another specific example: the problem of the total thrown on two dice.

We might begin by saying that the situation is described by noting that there are 11 possible results: totals ranging from 2 to 12, inclusive. This is a legitimate description of the situation in that any event concerned with totals (for example, the total is 2, the total is 2 or 9, the total is odd, etc.) will be some combination of these 11 results. However, Definition 1 is not directly applicable because we can find no legitimate excuse for calling these results equally likely; but we can use Definition 1 and the addition principle to formulate a law of probability to go with this 11 result situation.

On breaking the problem down further, we find results of a different kind which seem to be equally likely. These are the ordered pairs of numbers indicating the results on the individual dice. There are 36 of these, and they may be arranged in a very suggestive manner as follows:

(1,1)
(1,2), (2,1)
(1,3), (2,2), (3,1)
(1,4), (2,3), (3,2), (4,1)
(1,5), (2,4), (3,3), (4,2), (5,1)
(1,6), (2,5), (3,4), (4,3), (5,2), (6,1)
(2,6), (3,5), (4,4), (5,3), (6,2)
(3,6), (4,5), (5,4), (6,3)
(4,6), (5,5), (6,4)
(5,6), (6,5)
(6,6)

From this array, it is clear that Definition 1 gives us the following results:

Total:	2	3	4	5	6	7	8	9	10	11	12
Probability:	$\frac{1}{36}$	$\frac{2}{36}$	$\frac{3}{36}$	$\frac{4}{36}$	$\frac{5}{36}$	$\frac{6}{36}$	$\frac{5}{36}$	$\frac{4}{36}$	$\frac{3}{36}$	$\frac{2}{36}$	$\frac{1}{36}$

Now the addition principle gives us a law of probability applicable to all events admissible under the 11-result situation: To find the probability that the total is any one of a set of numbers taken from the set 2, 3, . . . , 12, add the probabilities given by the above table for the individual numbers in the set under consideration. Using this law, we find, for example, that the probability that the total is 5 or less is

$$\tfrac{1}{36} + \tfrac{2}{36} + \tfrac{3}{36} + \tfrac{4}{36} = \tfrac{5}{18}.$$

The probability that the total is odd is

$$\tfrac{2}{36} + \tfrac{4}{36} + \tfrac{6}{36} + \tfrac{4}{36} + \tfrac{2}{36} = \tfrac{1}{2}.$$

Probably the most important observation to be made concerning this example is that the general law of probability came directly from the table of probabilities for the individual numbers. In this case the table was obtained by using Definition 1; but, no matter how we arrived at such a table, it would still lead directly to a general formulation of the problem.

8. The Axiomatic Definition

In discussing roulette and dice we have chosen particular points for emphasis in order to call attention to the things that a mathematician expects of a law of probability. We might summarize these ideas as follows: As a basis for a discussion of probability there must be a fundamental set of "things" (numbers, number pairs, "results," or what have you). Every subset of this fundamental set will be called an event. Then, there should be a law of probability (usually called the probability distribution function or, frequently, simply the *distribution function*) which defines probability for each event. The addition principle should hold for this distribution function. Furthermore, the probability of each event should be a number between 0 and 1, and the probability of the entire fundamental set should be 1.

These properties of the distribution function are the ones ordinarily used to give a purely abstract, axiomatic definition of mathematical probability. Let us formulate them a little more precisely in the language of pure mathematics.

Let us think of the fundamental set of results as a set of points. In other words, let us construct a mathematical model of the physical situation in the form of a point set, each point of which represents one of the possible results of the experiment. The set of all such points to be considered in any given problem we shall call the *event space*. We shall designate this event space by S.

In the examples we have seen so far, the event space S has been a finite point set. In the roulette problem S contained 37 points; in the dice problem, 11 points. Indeed, in any problem directly covered by Definition 1, S will contain exactly n points. However, there is no need to restrict our purely mathematical model in this fashion; and it is here that we begin to transcend the elementary physical definition. Let us say, then, that an event space is any point set, finite or infinite.

The next step will be to define events as subsets of S; but, in the interest of being honest about it, we must point out that, in certain cases when the space has infinitely many points, not every subset should be called an event. In the terminology of modern integration theory, it is only the *measurable* subsets of S that we want to consider. This is no place to discuss the measurability of point sets. Instead, let us content ourselves with the following comments: The space S may contain:

(a) A *finite* number of points
(b) An *infinite sequence* of points—for example, the set of integer points on the real line
(c) A *continuum* of points—for example, the set of all points on a line or the set of all points in some line interval

In the first two cases, S is called *discrete*. In a discrete space all subsets are measurable. In the continuous case this is no longer true, but a nonmeasurable set is a very weird sort of thing—indeed, so unusual that it is of consequence only in advanced theoretical considerations in probability.

To return to our main line of discussion, we define an *event* as a measurable subset of S. Two events, E_1 and E_2, will be called *mutually exclusive* if they have no points in common. A (finite or infinite) collection of events will be called a collection of mutually exclusive events if no two of the events have a point in common. The *complement* of E, denoted by $\bar{E}$, is the set of all points of S not contained in E. If E_1 and E_2 are two point sets, we shall denote by $E_1 + E_2$ the set of all points belonging to either E_1 or E_2 (or both); we shall denote by E_1E_2

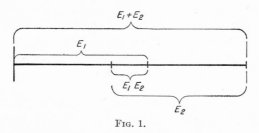

Fig. 1.

the set of points belonging to both E_1 and E_2. Naturally enough, the sets $E_1 + E_2$ and E_1E_2 are called the *sum* and *product*, respectively, of E_1 and E_2. We shall use ΣE_n and ΠE_n for the sum and product of any (finite or infinite) number of sets. The student should hardly need to be cautioned that addition and multiplication symbols may be applied to both sets and numbers in the course of a single formula and that their meaning depends on the type of thing to which they are applied.

At this stage, it might be a good idea to draw a parallel between the terminology of events considered as point sets in event space and that of events considered as results of a physical experiment:

Point Sets in Event Space	Results of a Physical Experiment
E is vacuous ($E = 0$)	E is logically impossible
$E = S$	E must occur
$E_1 + E_2$	The result is either E_1 or E_2
$E_1 E_2$	The result is both E_1 and E_2
E_1 and E_2 are mutually exclusive ($E_1 E_2 = 0$)	E_1 and E_2 are logically incompatible. If one occurs, the other does not
$\bar{E}$	E does not occur
E_2 is a subset of E_1	If E_2 occurs, so does E_1. E_2 implies E_1

Axiomatic Definition of Mathematical Probability. Given an event space S, $pr\{E\}$ will be called a probability distribution function for S if it satisfies the following axioms:

A. $pr\{E\} \geq 0$ for every event E of S.

B. $pr\{S\} = 1$.

C. If $E_1, E_2, E_3, \ldots$ is any (finite or infinite) sequence of mutually exclusive events of S, then

$$pr\{\Sigma E_n\} = \Sigma pr\{E_n\}.$$

These axioms are, for the most part, a repetition of the informal comments we made before, but in axiom C something new has been added. This is the fact that the addition principle should hold for infinite as well as finite collections of mutually exclusive events. So far as this course is concerned, our most common use of axiom C will be as a finite addition principle. Occasionally, however, we shall want to apply it to infinite sequences of mutually exclusive events; and the student should bear in mind that this extended addition principle is necessary for a completely satisfactory development of probability theory.

For a given space S there are many ways of constructing a distribution function $pr\{E\}$ satisfying the axioms. For example, if S is the set of numbers 2, 3, . . . , 12, we may assign a probability of $\frac{1}{11}$ to each point and use the addition principle to get a completely satisfactory distribution function. On the other hand, we have already seen that the assignment of probabilities we made in connection with the dice game accomplishes the same thing in a different way. The axioms merely tell us what a function must be like in order to be classed as a distribution function; the construction of the function in a specific problem will depend on the physical interpretation to be made of the mathematical model. But more of this later; first, let us look at some properties of the distribution function that are easily derived from the axioms.

Theorem I. If S is an event space and $pr\{E\}$ is a distribution function for S, then

(a) $pr\{\bar{E}\} = 1 - pr\{E\}$ for every E in S.

(b) The probability of the vacuous set is zero. $(pr\{0\} = 0.)$

(c) For every E in S, $0 \leq pr\{E\} \leq 1$.

(d) If E_2 is a subset of E_1, $pr\{E_1\} \geq pr\{E_2\}$.

(e) For any collection E_1, E_2, E_3, . . . (mutually exclusive or not), $pr\{\Sigma E_n\} \leq \Sigma pr\{E_n\}$.

The first four of these are almost obvious, but the student should check for himself that they follow directly from the axioms. With regard to (e), we might remark that the proof depends on the fact that, if any of the sets have points in common, the probability of these common points is counted only once on the left-hand side, but more than once on the right hand side. For more about sums of arbitrary sets, see Chap. 4.

One or two of these results deserve further comment. Referring to our table of parallels in terminology, we see that (b) says that, if an event is logically impossible, its probability is zero. This is very comforting, but it is important to note that the converse is not true. There are many examples (some of which we shall see very shortly) of events with probability zero which are by no means logically impossible. Finally, we should note that a very useful way of stating (d) is: If E_2 implies E_1, then $pr\{E_1\} \geq pr\{E_2\}$.

9. Stochastic Variables

So much for the abstract description of mathematical probability. The question that now arises is: What terminology and notation can we use to describe specific distribution functions? Can we write down formulas for them? If so, in terms of what?

A very useful notion in this connection is that of the *stochastic variable*. The word "stochastic" comes from a Greek stem meaning

chance.   The expressions "chance variable" and "random variable"
are also used by various authors as being synonymous with the expression "stochastic variable."   The general idea is this: Instead of trying
to describe a function $pr\{E\}$ over point sets, let us associate the points
of the event space S with numbers and then describe the distribution
function over sets of these numbers.   Now when we say, "Associate
the points of S with numbers," that is only another way of saying,
"Define a real-valued function over the points of S."   So the formal
definition of a stochastic variable is very simple.

Definition 2.   If S is an event space with a distribution function
attached and if x is a real-valued function defined over the points of S
(*i.e.*, to each point of S there corresponds a value of x), then x will be
called a stochastic variable.

Now, the distribution function for S automatically defines the probability of each value or set of values for x.   For instance, $pr\{x = a\}$
is the probability of the set in S for which $x = a$.   Similarly,
$pr\{a \leq x \leq b\}$ is the probability of the set of points in S for which
$a \leq x \leq b$.   However, this does not work the other way unless the
correspondence between points of S and values of x is 1 to 1.   Suppose
there are two points P and Q in S for which $x(P) = x(Q) = a$; then
$pr\{x = a\} = pr\{P + Q\}$, but this determines neither $pr\{P\}$ nor
$pr\{Q\}$.   Our present purpose is to see how a function of the stochastic
variable x can be defined so as to determine completely the distribution function for the event space S.   Therefore, for the remainder of
this chapter, we confine ourselves to a discussion of stochastic variables
for which the correspondence between points of S and values of x is
1 to 1.
This restricts the discussion in two ways.   First, the requirement
that the points of S be in 1-to-1 correspondence with a set of real
numbers means that S is (or might as well be) a set of points on a line.
In case it is impossible, impractical, or slightly undesirable to represent
the event space as a linear set, other methods of getting a complete
representation by means of stochastic variables will be called for.
These are discussed in Chap. 3.   But, even for event spaces on a line,
there are other stochastic variables than those given by 1-to-1 correspondences.   These, too, have their uses; and a more general discussion
of stochastic variables will be given in Chap. 5.
Suppose, then, that S is a set of points on a line.   The most obvious
way to associate numbers with these points is to think of the line as the

x axis and associate with each point its abscissa. The question of where we place the origin with respect to the set S is of no great importance for the present. Sometimes a strategic placing of the origin will simplify computations. More often, the origin is located so that the values of the variable x will have a useful physical significance. In any case, the usual plan is to decide what values we want x to run through and place the set S accordingly.

10. The Discrete Case

For the discrete case (a finite set or a sequence) the plan used in the dice problem will serve admirably. Let us define a function $f(x)$ such that, for each value a assumed by x, $f(a) = pr\{x = a\}$ (this probability to be determined by hook or crook or Definition 1 from the physical situation). Then, if E is any set of x values, we set

$$pr\{E\} = \sum_{x \text{ in } E} f(x).$$

It is an easy matter (which we leave to the student) to check that, if $f(x)$ is defined as we have suggested, the above formula gives a distribution function satisfying the axioms. Thus, for the discrete case, we have accomplished the end we had in mind. We have defined a function $f(x)$ of the stochastic variable x which describes completely the distribution function for the event space over which x is defined. We shall call $f(x)$ the *probability function* for the stochastic variable x.

If we take any function $f(x)$ and define from it a function of sets by adding the values of $f(x)$ over the set in question, the resulting function of sets will satisfy the addition axiom C. However, we get A if and only if we require that $f(x) \geq 0$ for every x; and B is equivalent to the condition $\sum_{x \text{ in } S} f(x) = 1$. Therefore, we might say that $f(x)$ will be called a probability function if it satisfies these two conditions. Let us summarize all these remarks as follows:

Theorem II. If $f(x)$ is a function defined over a discrete set S of values of x and if

(a) $\qquad\qquad\qquad f(x) \geq 0$ for every x in S,

(b) $\qquad\qquad\qquad \sum_{x \text{ in } S} f(x) = 1,$

then $f(x)$ is a probability function, and x is a stochastic variable with a distribution function given by the formula

(c) $$pr\{E\} = \sum_{x \text{ in } E} f(x).$$

Conversely, if x is a stochastic variable with a distribution function $pr\{E\}$, then a probability function $f(x)$ is given by the formula

(d) $$f(a) = pr\{x = a\} \text{ for each } a \text{ in } S.$$

All this is fairly obvious in the finite case. Even if S is an infinite sequence of points, the statements in Theorem II are easily checked provided that all infinite series encountered are convergent. Now, (b) says that $\sum_S f(x)$ is convergent; but we must deal with sums over subsets of S as well—i.e., with subseries of $\sum_S f(x)$. A necessary and sufficient condition that every subseries of $\sum_S f(x)$ be convergent is that this series itself be *absolutely convergent*—i.e., that $\sum_S |f(x)|$ be convergent. Condition (a) tells us that $|f(x)| = f(x)$ for each x; so the convergence guaranteed by (b) is automatically absolute convergence, and it follows that all subseries are convergent.

Theorem II suggests a practical way of representing a physical situation by a mathematical model. In the discrete case, if a probability function is fully described, the representation is complete. The significance of this remark is very graphically illustrated by the observation that in the roulette problem a complete tabulation of the probability function $f(x)$ would require only 37 entries, while a complete tabulation of the distribution function $pr\{E\}$ would require over 137 billion entries.

It should be clear from the above discussion how a stochastic variable representation can be constructed for a given physical situation, but the student might find it useful to have a systematic description of the steps involved.

Theorem III (*Working Rule*). To set up a discrete stochastic variable representing a given physical situation

(a) Take as values of x any set of numbers that seems appropriate, and devise a reasonable scheme for associating with each possible result of the experiment a value of x.

(*b*) Determine from the physical situation the probability of each of the results. Definition 1 may be useful in this step.

(*c*) Set $f(x)$ equal to the probability of the result represented by x.

11. Example—Balls from an Urn

To illustrate, step by step, the use of this rule, let us consider another simple example. An urn contains 5 red balls, 3 white balls, and 7 blue balls. One ball is to be drawn at random, and we shall be interested in the probability of its being a certain color. Represent this situation by a stochastic variable.

(*a*) We want to distinguish three possible results of the experiment; so we need three values for x. There being no particular reason for doing otherwise, we shall let these values be 1, 2, and 3 and associate them with the three possible results as follows:

1: A red ball is drawn
2: A white ball is drawn
3: A blue ball is drawn

(*b*) If we assume that each individual ball is as likely to be drawn as any other, Definition 1 tells us that the probability of drawing a red ball is $\frac{5}{15}$ or $\frac{1}{3}$. Similarly, that of drawing white is $\frac{1}{5}$; blue, $\frac{7}{15}$.

(*c*) Putting these results together, we define $f(x)$ by the following table:

$$x:\quad 1\quad 2\quad 3$$
$$f(x):\quad \tfrac{1}{3}\quad \tfrac{1}{5}\quad \tfrac{7}{15}$$

12. The Continuous Case

Turning, now, to the continuous case, suppose, first, that S is the entire x axis. The recollection that, if $f(x)$ is integrable,

$$\int_a^b f(x)dx + \int_b^c f(x)dx = \int_a^c f(x)dx$$

would suggest that an integral might give us a function of sets satisfying the addition axiom. Actually, if we think of an integral as it is introduced in first-year calculus, there are two things wrong with this suggestion. Such an integral cannot be defined over every measurable set, whereas a distribution function should be. Furthermore, there is trouble with the addition principle. This principle holds whenever all the integrals concerned are defined; but if we allow infinite sums, it may fail to make sense with probability defined as a Riemann (first-year calculus) integral. These are serious theoretical difficulties, but in this course we shall ignore them. This means that we shall set up an integral, call it a distribution function, and say it satisfies the axioms, whereas, actually, it does no such thing. Our justification for doing this is that there is a theory of integration, due largely to the French mathematician Lebesgue, which overcomes both these difficulties; and the modern theory of probability is developed in terms of these integrals.

In order to present a treatment representative of present-day theory of probability, we shall describe distribution functions as integrals. On the other hand, in order to stick to concepts familiar to the beginning student, we shall write all such integrals in the familiar form $\int_a^b f(x)dx$ or perhaps as multiple integrals of the type encountered in first-year calculus. The general effect of this is that we shall seem to assume that all events can be represented by intervals on the x axis. We trust that the student will realize that this is not actually the case; but we trust that he will benefit by having the mathematical development put in terms of concepts he understands.

Finally, we should like to reassure the student that, whenever the Riemann integral applies, it gives correct results. The Lebesgue theory does not introduce different mechanical procedures; it only covers a wider variety of cases.

Having decided, then, to set $pr\{E\} = \int_E f(x)dx$, what must we require of $f(x)$ in order to have axioms A and B satisfied? Clearly, A holds if and only if $f(x) \geq 0$ for every x; B says $\int_{-\infty}^{\infty} f(x)dx = 1$.

We have been operating so far on the assumption that S was the entire x axis. If we have a problem in which it seems advisable to use only a part of the line, we can set $f(x) = 0$ on the part we do not use, and all formulas will be perfectly correct. Therefore, these other continuous event spaces need no separate discussion.

So, again, we have a function $f(x)$ of the stochastic variable and an operation on that function which will determine all the values of the distribution function. In the continuous case, this function $f(x)$ is called the probability density function or, as a rule, just *density function*. We have thus developed the first half of a theorem for the continuous case similar to Theorem II for the discrete case. How about the second half? That is, given a distribution function, how do we find the density function? This is practically obvious; the distribution function is obtained by integrating the density function; so the density function must be the derivative of the distribution function. Let us now state our theorem.   The student should note the parallel between this and Theorem II.

Theorem IV.   If $f(x)$ is a function defined over the entire x axis and if

(a) $f(x) \geq 0$ for every x,

(b) $\int_{-\infty}^{\infty} f(x)dx = 1,$

then $f(x)$ is a density function, and x is a stochastic variable with a distribution function given by the formula

(c) $$pr\{E\} = \int_E f(x)dx.$$

Conversely, if x is a stochastic variable with a distribution function $pr\{E\}$ and if $F(t) = pr\{x \leq t\}$ is an indefinite integral, then a density function $f(x)$ is given by the formula

(d) $$f(x) = \frac{d}{dx}F(x).$$

Apropos the remark we made to the effect that probability zero does not necessarily mean logical impossibility, let us note that $\int_a^a f(x)dx = 0$; thus in the continuous case the probability of a single point is zero.   Furthermore, the sum of even an infinite sequence of zeros is still zero; therefore in the continuous case the probability of every discrete set is zero.   From this it follows that, if we talk about the probability that x is in a certain interval, it makes no difference whether or not we include the end points as part of the interval; that is, $pr\{a \leq x \leq b\} = pr\{a < x < b\}$.

There still remains the problem of finding a density function to go with a given physical situation.   Definition 1 is of no use whatsoever here, because it is limited by its very nature to the discrete case.   However, many continuous case problems are based on an idea very similar to that of equally likely results.   This is the idea of *choosing a point at random* on a line interval.   Just as with equally likely results, it is useless to try to define this phrase in physical terms.   The best we can do is state the continuous case parallel to Definition 1.

Definition **3.** If a point is chosen at random on a line interval of length A, the probability that it is in a given subinterval of length a is a/A.

It follows immediately from this that for a point chosen at random on the interval from 0 to A, the density function is equal to 0 outside the interval and $1/A$ inside. For, if $0 \leq t \leq A$, by Definition 3

$$pr\{x \leq t\} = pr\{0 \leq x \leq t\} = \frac{t}{A};$$

thus the distribution function is x/A, and its derivative is $1/A$. This disposes of a simple, yet important, special case; but it hardly suggests a general procedure for setting up the stochastic variable representations in the continuous case.

One such general procedure is suggested by the following observation:

$$pr\{t \leq x \leq t + dt\} = \int_t^{t+dt} f(x)dx,$$

and this integral is approximately equal to $f(t)dt$ (approximately equal in the sense that the error is an infinitesimal of higher order than dt). So, if the physical setup led us to an approximation to the probability that $t \leq x \leq t + dt$, and if we expressed our approximation in the form of a function of t multiplied by dt, then we might reasonably expect that this function would give us the proper form for the density function.

If we intend to use this suggestion, we should give some proof that it gives a function $f(x)$ that satisfies the conditions imposed in (*a*) and (*b*) of Theorem IV and that the application of Theorem IV yields probabilities consistent with those assumed in setting up the function. This is the type of proof we have decided to omit. For the benefit of those familiar with a rigorous definition of the Riemann integral, we might add that Duhamel's theorem will do the job without too much trouble. [See Franklin, *Treatise on Advanced Calculus*, New York (1940), pages 266 to 269.]

Another procedure that frequently works is that used above in the random point on a line problem. If we can dig up any information from the physical situation that will enable us to express $pr\{x \leq t\}$ as a function $F(t)$, then [by (*d*) of Theorem IV] the derivative of F gives us the density function. Again, let us give a formal summing up.

Theorem V (*Working Rule*). In the continuous case, to represent a physical situation by a stochastic variable

(a) Represent the set of all possible results in some orderly fashion by some set of values for x.   The set of x values used may or may not be the whole real number system.

(b) Dispose of any unused x values immediately by setting $f(x) = 0$ for these values.

Then, proceed to (c) and (d) or to (c') and (d').

(c) For t and $t + dt$ both lying in the set of x values that represent results, figure out from the physical situation an approximation to the probability that $t \leq x \leq t + dt$.   Express the result in the form $f(t)dt$.

(d) Take the function $f(t)$ from (c); replace the t by x; use the resulting function $f(x)$ as a density function.

(c') For t in the set of x values that represent results, figure out from the physical situation the probability that $x \leq t$.   Express the result in the form $F(t)$.

(d') Take the function $F(t)$ from (c'); replace the t by x; differentiate with respect to x.   This derivative will be the density function.

With regard to the word "approximation" in (c), it should be added that it must be an approximation for which the error is an infinitesimal of higher order than dt.   Many first-year calculus books give the subject of order of infinitesimals only the "once over lightly" treatment; so while this is a precise description of what is required, it might be of more interest to the student to note that the choice of this approximation is governed by the same rules as those which govern the choice of approximations to increments of area, volume, work, etc., in setting up definite integrals.   In fact, steps (c) and (d) are just another first-year calculus exercise in setting up definite integrals.

13. Example—Bombardment of Hemispherical Screen

To illustrate step by step the use of Theorem V, let us consider the following problem: A hemispherical screen is bombarded by a stream of electrons (see sketch).   It is assumed that the radial distribution of

Fig. 2.

electrons is uniform and that all electrons considered hit the screen. Set up a density function that will determine probabilities as to the colatitude φ of the point at which a given electron, chosen at random, will hit. (a) For obvious reasons, we shall call the stochastic variable φ in this case. Results will then be represented by the values of φ from 0 to $\pi/2$. (b) According to instructions, we set $f(\varphi) = 0$ for $\varphi < 0$ and for $\varphi > \pi/2$. (c) The event $t \leq \varphi \leq t + dt$ is equivalent (see sketch) to the event that the radial distance falls in an interval of length r; therefore its probability is r/R. Now, $r = s \cos t$, and s is approximately $R\,dt$; hence $r/R \simeq \cos t\,dt$. (d) Replacing t by φ, we have the density function $f(\varphi) = \cos \varphi$.

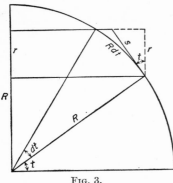

FIG. 3.

14. Example—The Radium Atom

To illustrate the primed version of Theorem V, we might try the problem of the radium atom. It has been verified experimentally that the time rate of decomposition of a quantity of radium is proportional to the mass. That is,

$$\frac{dm}{dt} = -km.$$

Furthermore, it is known that the mass is halved in 1,580 years. Thus, if we have mass m_0 at $t = 0$, we have mass $m_0/2$ at $t = 1,580$. Armed with this information, we can find m in terms of t:

$$\frac{dm}{m} = -k\,dt.$$

Integrating, we get

$$\log m = -kt + C.$$

From the condition $m = m_0$ at $t = 0$, we have

$$C = \log m_0.$$

From the condition $m = m_0/2$ at $t = 1,580$, we have

$$k = \frac{\log 2}{1,580}.$$

Thus,

$$m = m_0 e^{-(\log 2/1,580)t},$$

and the fraction of the original mass that disintegrates from time 0 to time t is

$$\frac{m_0 - m}{m_0} = 1 - e^{-(\log 2/1,580)t}.$$

Now, if this is what happens in the aggregate, we might take it as a reasonable indication of the probability that a given atom will disintegrate before time t.

So, to follow through the steps in Theorem V, suppose we are given an atom of radium at time 0. (a) Let x stand for the time it disintegrates. (b) We want only the positive half of the x axis; so we set $f(x) = 0$ for $x \leq 0$. (c') On the basis of the argument above, we agree that

$$pr\{x \leq t\} = 1 - e^{-(\log 2/1,580)t}.$$

(d') Substituting and differentiating, we get the density function

$$f(x) = \frac{d}{dx}(1 - e^{-kx}) = ke^{-kx}$$

where $k = (\log 2)/1,580$.

15. Synthesis of Discrete and Continuous Cases

In succeeding chapters we shall prove a number of theorems about probabilities and related quantities. Many of these proofs will be based on the analytical representation of mathematical probability. Unfortunately, however, we have two such representations, (c) of Theorem II and (c) of Theorem IV. There is no way of consolidating the two for purposes of making direct computations. If we want to find a specific probability from a stochastic variable representation, in the discrete case we must add. In the continuous case we must integrate. However, there is a thing called a Stieltjes integral which has as special cases ordinary integrals, finite sums, and infinite series. So the two representations could be consolidated into a single formula involving a Stieltjes integral. This procedure would serve to unify subsequent theoretical discussions but would have no effect whatever on the nature of the computations involved in a specific problem.

We shall not attempt to use Stieltjes integrals in this course because we want to stick to analytic forms that are familiar to the first-year calculus student; so everything we discuss will come in two cases. Rather than give two proofs of each theorem, we shall usually present the theory for the continuous case only. Of course, many of the examples and exercises will fit the discrete case. Therefore, for everything we do with integrals, the student might do well to run through an analogous operation with sums. We have chosen to present our discussion in terms of integrals for two reasons: first, many of the fundamental relationships stand out more clearly when presented in this form; second, we want to accustom the student to thinking of probability as an integral because it appears in that form in advanced treatises on the subject.

One thing we lose by not using Stieltjes integrals is the consideration of the so-called mixed case. Suppose $f(x) \geq 0$ and $\int_{-\infty}^{\infty} f(x)dx = \frac{1}{2}$. Then, let us take some point x_0 and set $pr\{x = x_0\} = \frac{1}{2}$. Now, let us define $pr\{E\}$ as $\int_E f(x)dx$ provided that E does not contain x_0, and let $pr\{E\} = \frac{1}{2} + \int_E f(x)dx$ if E contains x_0. This distribution function clearly satisfies the axioms, but it is not described by either a discrete probability function or a density function. Having mentioned this possibility, we shall now proceed to ignore it. The only satisfactory description of all such cases (they can be much more complicated than the above example) is a Lebesgue-Stieltjes integral. So here is one more way in which our treatment of probability theory—though representative in at least a formal sense—is definitely restricted in the interests of mathematical simplicity.

For the benefit of the student who is interested in persuing this subject further, we might add that the chapters of Cramér's book listed below contain an excellent discussion of the Lebesgue-Stieltjes integral, designed specifically as an introduction to probability theory.

REFERENCES FOR FURTHER STUDY

Coolidge, *An Introduction to Mathematical Probability*, Oxford (1925), Chap. I.

Cramér, *Mathematical Methods of Statistics*, Princeton (1946), Chaps. 1–7, 13, 14.

Kolmogoroff, *Foundations of the Theory of Probability*, New York (1950).

Levy and Roth, *Elements of Probability*, Chaps. I, II, IV, VI.

Struik, "On the Foundations of the Theory of Probability," *Philosophy of Science* (1934), vol. 1, pp. 50–70.

Uspensky, *Introduction to Mathematical Probability*, New York (1937), Introduction, Chaps. I, II, XII, XIII.

PROBLEMS

1. What is the probability of throwing 8, 9, or 10 with 2 dice?

Ans. $\frac{1}{3}$.

2. What is the probability of throwing 6 or less with 3 dice?

Ans. $\frac{5}{54}$.

3. A set of pool balls (15 balls numbered 1 to 15) is placed in an urn, and 2 balls are drawn simultaneously. What is the probability that the sum of their numbers is 10? *Ans.* $\frac{4}{105}$.

4. If, in Prob. 3, one ball is drawn and replaced and then the second is drawn, what is the probability that the sum of the numbers is 10? *Ans.* $\frac{1}{25}$.

5. In Prob. 3, what is the probability that the product of the numbers is 10? What is the probability of this event in Prob. 4? *Ans.* $\frac{2}{105}$, $\frac{4}{225}$.

6. A roulette player places 3 bets on one spin of the wheel: 1 on rows 4 and 5 (numbers 10 to 15), 1 on the first column, and 1 on red. What is the probability that at least 1 of these will win? that the first 2 mentioned will win? that all 3 will win? *Ans.* $\frac{26}{37}$, $\frac{2}{37}$, 0.

7. Four tickets numbered 1, 2, 3, 4 are placed in an urn and drawn out one at a time (without replacements). They are renumbered in the order in which they are drawn. What is the probability that all 4 numbers are changed? *Ans.* $\frac{3}{8}$.

8. Find the probability of being dealt each of the following poker hands: 1 pair, 2 pairs, 3 of a kind, full house, 4 of a kind.
Ans. $\frac{352}{833}$; 198/4,165; 88/4,165; 6/4,165; 1/4,165.

9. A poker hand contains 4 cards of one suit and 1 odd card. If the odd card is discarded and 1 card drawn from the remainder of the deck, what is the probability of filling the flush—getting a fifth card of the given suit? *Ans.* $\frac{9}{47}$.

10. A poker hand contains 4 cards in sequence (not A234 or JQKA) and 1 odd card. If the odd card is discarded and 1 card drawn from the remainder of the deck, what is the probability of filling the straight? (A straight is a 5-card sequence, not necessarily all of the same suit.) *Ans.* $\frac{8}{47}$.

11. What is the probability of filling an "inside" straight? The hand contains 4 of a 5-card sequence with a gap in the middle (for example, 4578); the odd card is discarded and 1 card drawn from the remainder of the deck. *Ans.* $\frac{4}{47}$.

12. A poker hand contains a 4-card sequence (as in Prob. 10) all in the same suit. If 1 card is drawn, what is the probability of filling either the straight or the flush? *Ans.* $\frac{15}{47}$.

13. Let x represent the number of aces in a single 13-card bridge hand. Find the probability function for the stochastic variable x.

Ans.

x:	0	1	2	3	4
$f(x)$:	$\dfrac{^{48}C_{13}}{^{52}C_{13}}$	$\dfrac{4 \cdot {^{48}C_{12}}}{^{52}C_{13}}$	$\dfrac{6 \cdot {^{48}C_{11}}}{^{52}C_{13}}$	$\dfrac{4 \cdot {^{48}C_{10}}}{^{52}C_{13}}$	$\dfrac{^{48}C_{9}}{^{52}C_{13}}$

14. What is the probability that a bridge hand will contain no more than 1 ace? *Ans.* $\frac{88}{49} \cdot {^{49}C_{13}}/{^{52}C_{13}}$.

15. Two urns contain, respectively, 3 white, 5 red, 12 black balls and 8 white, 3 red, 9 black balls. One ball is drawn from each urn. Represent the 9 (ordered) color combinations by a stochastic variable, and find its probability function.

Ans. x: 1   2   3   4   5   6   7   8   9

$f(x)$: $24/400$ $9/400$ $27/400$ $40/400$ $15/400$ $45/400$ $96/400$ $36/400$ $108/400$

Note: The student should indicate the significance of each value of x.

16. From the results in Prob. 15, find the probability that neither ball was black; that they were not both black.   *Ans.* $11/50$, $73/100$.

17. Three balls numbered 1, 2, 3 are placed in an urn. A ball is drawn and replaced; then another ball is drawn. Let the stochastic variable x represent the sum of the 2 numbers drawn. Find the probability function for x.   *Ans.* x: 2   3   4   5   6

$f(x)$: $1/9$ $2/9$ $1/3$ $2/9$ $1/9$

18. Suppose the second drawing is made without replacing the first ball. Find the probability function for the sum of the numbers drawn.

Ans. x: 3   4   5

$f(x)$: $1/3$ $1/3$ $1/3$

19. From this same urn the balls are drawn as in Prob. 17. Find the probability function for the product of the numbers drawn.

Ans. x: 1   2   3   4   6   9

$f(x)$: $1/9$ $2/9$ $2/9$ $1/9$ $2/9$ $1/9$

20. Find the probability function for the product of the numbers drawn when the drawings are made as in Prob. 18.

Ans. x: 2   3   6

$f(x)$: $1/3$ $1/3$ $1/3$

21. An urn contains 10 white balls and 10 black balls. Five balls are drawn simultaneously. Find the probability function for the number of white balls drawn.

Ans. x: 0   1   2   3   4   5

$f(x)$: $\dfrac{252}{15,504}$ $\dfrac{2,100}{15,504}$ $\dfrac{5,400}{15,504}$ $\dfrac{5,400}{15,504}$ $\dfrac{2,100}{15,504}$ $\dfrac{252}{15,504}$

22. The stochastic variable x can assume the values $0, 1, 2, \ldots, n$ with $pr\{x = r\}$ proportional to ^nC_r. Find the probability function for x. Hint: Axiom B must be satisfied.   *Ans.* $f(x) = {}^nC_x/2^n$.

23. The stochastic variable x can assume the values $0, 1, 2, 3, \ldots$ with $pr\{x = r\}$ proportional to $a^r/r!$. Find the probability function for x.   *Ans.* $f(x) = a^x e^{-a}/x!$ (Poisson's distribution).

24. The stochastic variable x can assume the values $1, 2, \ldots, n$ with $pr\{x = r\}$ proportional to r. Find the probability function for x.

Ans. $f(x) = 2x/n(n + 1)$.

25. A radio station broadcasts the correct time every hour on the hour. What is the probability that a listener tuning in at random will have to wait less than 10 minutes to get the correct time? *Ans.* ⅙.

26. A point is chosen at random on a line segment, dividing it into 2 segments. Find the probability that the ratio of the length of the left-hand segment to that of the right-hand one is less than a given number α. *Ans.* $\alpha/(1 + \alpha)$.

27. In Prob. 26, what is the probability that the ratio of the length of the right-hand segment to that of the left-hand one is less than α? *Ans.* $\alpha/(1 + \alpha)$.

28. In Prob. 26, what is the probability that the length of the shorter segment to that of the longer one is less than ⅓? *Ans.* ½.

29. Given an atom of radium at the beginning of a leap year, find the probability that it will disintegrate during a leap year. (Use a Julian calendar—*every* fourth year a leap year.)
Ans. $(1 - e^{-k})/(1 - e^{-4k})$; $k = (\log 2)/1{,}580$.

30. A point is chosen at random on a semicircle and projected onto the diameter. Find the density function for the point of projection.
Ans. $f(x) = 1/\pi \sqrt{1 - x^2}$ for $-1 < x < 1$, $f(x) = 0$ otherwise.

31. An angle θ is chosen at random between $-\pi/2$ and $\pi/2$ and a line is drawn through the point $(0,1)$ at the angle θ with the y axis. Find the density function for the point x at which this line crosses the x axis. *Ans.* $f(x) = 1/\pi(1 + x^2)$ (Cauchy's distribution).

32. A number is chosen at random between 0 and 1. What is the probability that its first decimal place is a 7? that its second decimal place is a 7? that the nth place is a 7? *Ans.* ⅒ in each case.

33. A number is chosen at random between 0 and 1. What is the probability that its first 2 decimal places are 7's? that any 2 specified decimal places are 7's? *Ans.* 1/100 in each case.

34. A number is chosen at random between 0 and 1. What is the probability that it has a 7 in each of k specified decimal places?
Ans. $1/10^k$.

Note: Problems 33 and 34 should be solved directly from Definition 3. See comment, Prob. 33, Chap. 3.

35. A number is chosen at random between 0 and 1. Let x_n be the nth decimal place. Find the probability function for x_n.
Ans. $f(x_n) = \frac{1}{10}$; $x_n = 0, 1, 2, \ldots, 9$.

36. Prove Theorem I, using only the axioms. Outline: (*a*) follows from Axioms *B* and *C*; (*b*) follows from (*a*) and Axiom *B*; (*c*) follows from (*a*) and Axiom *A*; (*d*) follows from Axioms *A* and *C*; (*e*) may be proved by induction, using Axiom *C* and (*d*).

CHAPTER 3

JOINT DISTRIBUTIONS

In the previous chapter we discussed the representation of a situation by a single stochastic variable. Such a representation amounts to lining the possible events up in a row and assigning abscissas to them (and then, of course, computing a suitable density function). Now, there are situations in which such a linear array of the possible events does not adequately describe all the similarities and interrelationships among them. For instance, in the throwing of 2 dice, we might want to list as the set of possible events the set of all ordered pairs of numbers that might show up. These could be laid out in a row and numbered in some orderly fashion, but such a set of events is just crying to be arranged in a 6 × 6 square array. Perhaps this point is even better illustrated by Prob. 15, Chap. 2. There each event consists of a pair of colors (9 such pairs in all). These, too, could be laid out in a row and numbered (and that is what we suggested in the answer we gave), but is it not much more natural to arrange these pairs in a 3 × 3 square array? If we had 3 urns containing 3 colors each, we should be led in the same manner to a 3 × 3 × 3 cubical arrangement.

Granted, then, that there are situations for which sets of points in two or more dimensions give better representations than linear sets. We shall take the hint and develop a theory of two or more stochastic variables. One thing we might note to begin with is that, when we use a multidimensional representation of a physical situation, we describe each basic event (point) in the space as a logical product of two or more events. That is, if A is the event $x = x_0$ and B is the event $y = y_0$, then the point (x_0, y_0) is the event AB. We shall frequently refer to such product events as *compound events*. The individual events of which a compound event is the product we shall call its *component events*. We might add that "compoundness" is not an intrinsic property of physical events. We use the phrase only to distinguish certain events in a physical situation for which a multidimensional event space seems to be the natural representation.

16. Joint Density Functions

In the interest of making ideas clearer by keeping the notation simpler, we shall confine most of our discussion in this chapter to the two-dimensional case—*i.e.*, the case in which each compound event has two components. The student who conquers this two-dimensional discussion should have no trouble in following through all the steps for as many variables as he pleases.

Suppose the event space S is a two-dimensional set. Events will be measurable subsets of S, and the axioms will be expected to apply verbatim. To get a stochastic variable representation, let x and y be rectangular coordinates in the plane in which S lies. Then, x and y are functions of the points of S, so each is a stochastic variable (Definition 2, Chap. 2). To describe the distribution function $pr\{E\}$ in terms of a function $\varphi(x,y)$, let us note that a double integral of φ satisfies the addition principle. Therefore, all we need is a pair of conditions on $\varphi(x,y)$ to guarantee the satisfaction of Axioms A and B. Obviously, these are $\varphi(x,y) \geq 0$, and $\int_{-\infty}^{\infty} \int_{-\infty}^{\infty} \varphi(x,y)dx\,dy = 1$. Such a function $\varphi(x,y)$ we shall call a *joint density function*. The distribution function $pr\{E\}$ that it generates we shall call the *joint distribution function* for x and y.

This gives us the first half of a theorem similar to Theorem IV, Chap. 2. The second half [a formula for the joint density function $\varphi(x,y)$ in terms of the distribution function $pr\{E\}$] is obtained by noting that the inverse operator to a double integral is a cross partial derivative. That is, if

$$\Phi(u,v) = \int_{-\infty}^{v} \int_{-\infty}^{u} \varphi(x,y)dx\,dy,$$

then

$$\varphi(u,v) = \frac{\partial^2 \Phi}{\partial u\,\partial v}.$$

One more remark is called for before we give a formal statement of these results. We can always speak of $\varphi(x,y)$ as being defined over the entire xy plane. If S is not the whole plane, we set $\varphi(x,y) = 0$ outside S.

Theorem I. If $\varphi(x,y)$ is a function defined over the entire xy plane and if

(a) $\qquad\qquad\qquad \varphi(x,y) \geq 0$ for every x, y,

(b) $\qquad\qquad\quad \int_{-\infty}^{\infty} \int_{-\infty}^{\infty} \varphi(x,y)dx\,dy = 1$,

then $\varphi(x,y)$ is a joint density function, and x and y are stochastic variables with a joint distribution function given by the formula

(c) $\qquad\qquad\qquad pr\{E\} = \int \int_{E} \varphi(x,y)dx\,dy.$

In particular,

(d) $\qquad pr\{a \leq x \leq b \text{ and } c \leq y \leq d\} = \int_c^d \int_a^b \varphi(x,y)dx\, dy.$

Conversely, if x and y are stochastic variables with a joint distribution function $pr\{E\}$ and if $\Phi(u,v) = pr\{x \leq u \text{ and } y \leq v\}$ is an indefinite double integral, then a joint density function $\varphi(x,y)$ is given by the formula

(e) $\qquad\qquad\qquad \varphi(x,y) = \dfrac{\partial^2 \Phi(x,y)}{\partial x\, \partial y}.$

Many times, in what follows, we shall have occasion to reverse the order of integration in a double integral. We shall do this without calling any particular attention to it. A word should be said here about the justification for this procedure, particularly since we are so often dealing with improper integrals. The standard theorem on this is that the order of integration may be reversed if the integral is absolutely convergent (see Franklin, *Treatise on Advanced Calculus*, page 398.) Now (a) of Theorem I means that any convergence of integrals of φ is absolute convergence, and (b) says (among other things) that all integrals of φ are convergent. So, as long as φ is our only integrand, we may change the order of integration at will. Later on (Chap. 6) we shall have other integrands to deal with, but we shall make our definitions in such a way that absolute convergence is still guaranteed.

As we noted at the end of Chap. 2, we shall develop the theory in terms of the continuous case. However, we might do well to state the discrete case parallel to Theorem I.

Theorem II. If $\varphi(x,y)$ is a function defined over a discrete set S of points in the xy plane and if

(a) $\qquad\qquad \varphi(x,y) \geq 0$ for every point (x,y) in S,

(b) $\qquad\qquad\qquad \displaystyle\sum_{(x,y) \text{ in } S} \sum \varphi(x,y) = 1,$

then $\varphi(x,y)$ is a joint probability function, and x and y are stochastic variables with a joint distribution function given by the formula

(c) $\qquad\qquad pr\{E\} = \displaystyle\sum_{(x,y) \text{ in } E} \sum \varphi(x,y).$

In particular,

(d) $\qquad\qquad pr\{x = x_0 \text{ and } y = y_0\} = \varphi(x_0,y_0).$

Conversely, if x and y are discrete stochastic variables with a joint distribution function $pr\{E\}$, then a joint probability function $\varphi(x,y)$ is given by (d).

17. Marginal Distributions

We now raise the question whether stochastic variables described by a joint density function have their own density functions as in Theorem IV, Chap. 2. This is, indeed, the case; and these individual density functions are determined by the joint density function. Note that the single pair of inequalities $a \le x \le b$ describes an entire vertical strip in the xy plane; so

$$pr\{a \le x \le b\} = \int_{-\infty}^{\infty} \int_{a}^{b} \varphi(x,y)dx\, dy = \int_{a}^{b} \int_{-\infty}^{\infty} \varphi(x,y)dy\, dx$$
$$= \int_{a}^{b} f(x)dx,$$

where

$$f(x) = \int_{-\infty}^{\infty} \varphi(x,y)dy.$$

It is now easily seen that $f(x)$ will serve as a density function for the stochastic variable x. (Set $a = t$, $b = t + dt$, and apply Theorem V, Chap. 2.) Similarly, we may obtain the density function

$$g(y) = \int_{-\infty}^{\infty} \varphi(x,y)dx.$$

These individual density functions $f(x)$ and $g(y)$ are called the *marginal density functions*, and the distribution functions they generate by means of (c) of Theorem IV, Chap. 2, are called the *marginal distributions*. This terminology probably comes from the fact that in the finite case a convenient way of describing $\varphi(x,y)$ is to write its values out in a square array. Then, $f(x)$ and $g(y)$ are given by adding the columns and rows, respectively; and the values of these functions are very conveniently listed around the margins of the square array.

It should be emphasized that any discussion of two stochastic variables is based primarily on the joint density function and not on the marginal density functions. While we have just seen that the joint density function determines the marginal ones, the reverse is not true at all. It is very easy to find two fundamentally different joint density functions each of which gives rise to the same pair of marginal density functions. Consider, for instance,

$$\varphi_1(x,y) = \begin{cases} x + y & \text{for } 0 \le x \le 1 \text{ and } 0 \le y \le 1, \\ 0 & \text{otherwise;} \end{cases}$$
$$\varphi_2(x,y) = \begin{cases} (\tfrac{1}{2} + x)(\tfrac{1}{2} + y) & \text{for } 0 \le x \le 1 \text{ and } 0 \le y \le 1, \\ 0 & \text{otherwise.} \end{cases}$$

The equation $(\frac{1}{2} + x)(\frac{1}{2} + y) = x + y$ has for its only roots $x = \frac{1}{2}$, $y = \frac{1}{2}$; thus, inside the unit square, $\varphi_1(x,y) = \varphi_2(x,y)$ only along two lines. However, each will pass as a joint density function, and each leads to the same pair of marginal density functions:

$$f_1(x) = \int_{-\infty}^{\infty} \varphi_1(x,y)dy = \int_0^1 (x + y)dy = \frac{1}{2} + x;$$

$$f_2(x) = \int_{-\infty}^{\infty} \varphi_2(x,y)dy = \int_0^1 (\frac{1}{2} + x)(\frac{1}{2} + y)dy = \frac{1}{2} + x;$$

$$g_1(y) = \int_{-\infty}^{\infty} \varphi_1(x,y)dx = \int_0^1 (x + y)dx = \frac{1}{2} + y;$$

$$g_2(y) = \int_{-\infty}^{\infty} \varphi_2(x,y)dx = \int_0^1 (\frac{1}{2} + x)(\frac{1}{2} + y)dx = \frac{1}{2} + y.$$

18. Example—Two Dice

As for representing physical situations by pairs of stochastic variables, the procedure is roughly the same as that outlined in Chap. 2 for getting one-variable representations. The general principle is that, if we know the probabilities of all the events involved, the density function is arrived at in the usual manner. The only real question then concerns finding the probability of a compound event. Now, in many cases this can be done by inspection or by a direct application of Definition 1, Chap. 2, to the compound events themselves. The problem of the two dice is one that can be done by inspection. Let us look at it by way of illustration of the ideas presented so far.

We think of each result of throwing 2 dice as a compound event composed of 1 result on one die and 1 on the other. Now, let x represent the result on one die and y the result on the other. There are 6 possible results on each die: so we give x the values 1, 2, . . . , 6 and do the same for y. This gives us 36 points in the xy plane, each of which represents 1 of our compound events. Now (and this is what we meant by doing it by inspection), these compound events seem equally likely; so we give them each a weight of $\frac{1}{36}$. That is, we set $\varphi(x,y) = \frac{1}{36}$ for each of the 36 points at which it is to be defined.

In this, as in any other finite case, an integral from $-\infty$ to ∞ is replaced by a finite sum (for this particular situation, a sum of 6 terms). A double integral over an area will consist of the sum of all φ values for points found in that area. Bearing these points in mind, we might carry out a few of the operations on joint density functions already discussed. The accompanying chart shows the values of $\varphi(x,y)$ at appropriate places in the plane. The rows and columns are added to give the marginal probability functions. Finally, the values of x and y are listed around the outside.

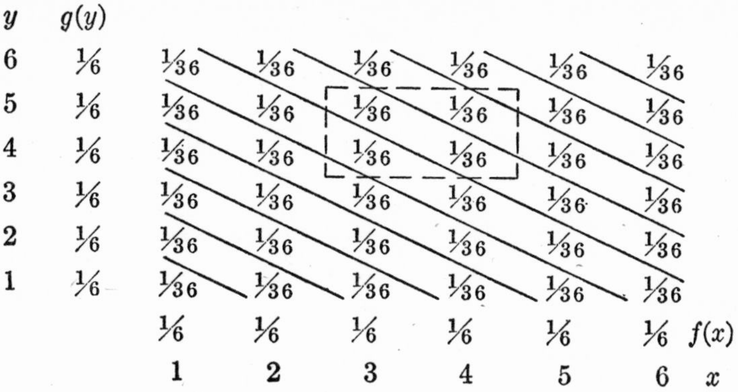

y	$g(y)$						
6	$\frac{1}{6}$	$\frac{1}{36}$	$\frac{1}{36}$	$\frac{1}{36}$	$\frac{1}{36}$	$\frac{1}{36}$	$\frac{1}{36}$
5	$\frac{1}{6}$	$\frac{1}{36}$	$\frac{1}{36}$	$\frac{1}{36}$	$\frac{1}{36}$	$\frac{1}{36}$	$\frac{1}{36}$
4	$\frac{1}{6}$	$\frac{1}{36}$	$\frac{1}{36}$	$\frac{1}{36}$	$\frac{1}{36}$	$\frac{1}{36}$	$\frac{1}{36}$
3	$\frac{1}{6}$	$\frac{1}{36}$	$\frac{1}{36}$	$\frac{1}{36}$	$\frac{1}{36}$	$\frac{1}{36}$	$\frac{1}{36}$
2	$\frac{1}{6}$	$\frac{1}{36}$	$\frac{1}{36}$	$\frac{1}{36}$	$\frac{1}{36}$	$\frac{1}{36}$	$\frac{1}{36}$
1	$\frac{1}{6}$	$\frac{1}{36}$	$\frac{1}{36}$	$\frac{1}{36}$	$\frac{1}{36}$	$\frac{1}{36}$	$\frac{1}{36}$
		$\frac{1}{6}$	$\frac{1}{6}$	$\frac{1}{6}$	$\frac{1}{6}$	$\frac{1}{6}$	$\frac{1}{6}$ $f(x)$
		1	2	3	4	5	6 x

FIG. 4.

To apply (c) of Theorem II, we could write

$$pr\{3 \leq x \leq 4 \text{ and } 4 \leq y \leq 5\} = \sum_{x=3}^{4} \sum_{y=4}^{5} \varphi(x,y) = \frac{4}{36} = \frac{1}{9}$$

(area outlined by dotted line). However, the house pays off on the sum of x and y; hence the events we are most interested in are those represented by the areas between diagonal lines. To compute these, the formality of a double sum is unduly laborious; so we dispense with it and merely add down the diagonal strips to get the usual table:

$x + y$:	2	3	4	5	6	7	8	9	10	11	12
pr:	$\frac{1}{36}$	$\frac{2}{36}$	$\frac{3}{36}$	$\frac{4}{36}$	$\frac{5}{36}$	$\frac{6}{36}$	$\frac{5}{36}$	$\frac{4}{36}$	$\frac{3}{36}$	$\frac{2}{36}$	$\frac{1}{36}$

It appears from this that the stochastic variable we used to describe the two dice in Chap. 2 is the sum of the two variables we are using here. This is of more than just passing interest. In later chapters we shall have quite a lot to say about sums of stochastic variables, and the student will want to learn what is meant by such a sum and what significance can be attached to it. These questions are discussed at some length in Chap. 5, but the example given here might serve as a starting point for the student's thinking on the subject.

19. Conditional Probabilities

In setting up the joint probability function in the preceding example, we took a quick look at the compound events and decided on their probabilities directly. Now, in many situations this is not feasible; so we turn our attention to the problem of working up from an analysis of the component events to a determination of probabilities for the compound events. As we noted above, a knowledge of the marginal density functions will not suffice, because these do not determine the joint density function uniquely; and two stochastic variables are not adequately described unless the joint density function is given.

So we need a new idea; and this idea turns out to be that of *conditional probability*. This notion is described by the following problem: Given $a \leq x \leq b$, what is the probability that $c \leq y \leq d$? The answer will be found in the usual manner [from (d) of Theorem I] once we obtain a new joint density function $\psi(x,y)$ which describes our hypotheses. Since all events for which $x < a$ or $x > b$ are to be ruled out, we set $\psi(x,y) = 0$ over these portions of the xy plane. In the strip $a \leq x \leq b$ we want x and y related as before; so we set $\psi(x,y) = k\varphi(x,y)$ over this strip. Now, ψ is determined as soon as we find the constant k. Noting that we must have

$$1 = \int_{-\infty}^{\infty} \int_{-\infty}^{\infty} \psi(x,y)dx \, dy = \int_{-\infty}^{\infty} \int_{a}^{b} k\varphi(x,y)dx \, dy$$

$$= k \int_{a}^{b} \int_{-\infty}^{\infty} \varphi(x,y)dy \, dx = k \int_{a}^{b} f(x)dx,$$

it appears that

$$k = \frac{1}{\int_{a}^{b} f(x)dx}.$$

Now, using (d) of Theorem I, we have that, given $a \leq x \leq b$,

$$pr\{c \leq y \leq d\} = \int_{c}^{d} \int_{-\infty}^{\infty} \psi(x,y)dx \, dy$$

$$= \int_{c}^{d} \left[\frac{\int_{a}^{b} \varphi(x,y)dx}{\int_{a}^{b} f(x)dx} \right] dy.$$

The expression in brackets will be called the *conditional density function* for y:

$$g_{a,b}(y) = \frac{\int_{a}^{b} \varphi(x,y)dx}{\int_{a}^{b} f(x)dx}.$$

The conditional probabilities we mentioned will then be given by integrals of this conditional density function. Our notation for conditional probabilities will have the condition described in a subscript; thus the probability that $c \leq y \leq d$, given that $a \leq x \leq b$, would be written

$$pr_{a \leq x \leq b}\{c \leq y \leq d\}.$$

To save ink, we shall frequently abbreviate this to

$$pr_{a,b}\{c \leq y \leq d\}.$$

In this notation,

$$pr_{a,b}\{c \leq y \leq d\} = \int_c^d g_{a,b}(y)dy.$$

The other set of conditional probabilities (probabilities for x, given information about y) are defined in a similar manner. Let us collect these notions and state them formally as follows:

Definition 1.   Let $\varphi(x,y)$ be the joint density function for a pair of stochastic variables x and y, and let

$$f(x) = \int_{-\infty}^{\infty} \varphi(x,y)dy \qquad \text{and} \qquad g(y) = \int_{-\infty}^{\infty} \varphi(x,y)dx$$

be the corresponding marginal density functions. Then the conditional density functions are defined as

$$(a) \qquad f_{c,d}(x) = \frac{\int_c^d \varphi(x,y)dy}{\int_c^d g(y)dy}, \qquad g_{a,b}(y) = \frac{\int_a^b \varphi(x,y)dx}{\int_a^b f(x)dx}.$$

Conditional probabilities for x and y are defined by

$$(b) \quad pr_{c,d}\{a \leq x \leq b\} = \int_a^b f_{c,d}(x)dx,$$

$$pr_{a,b}\{c \leq y \leq d\} = \int_c^d g_{a,b}(y)dy.$$

In the discrete case, probabilities of single values for x and y are different from zero; and the usual form for conditional probabilities is sufficiently different to be worth mentioning. Note that, with the usual transposition of integrals into sums, Definition 1 describes the discrete situation too. The following is merely an important special case:

Theorem III.   Let $\varphi(x,y)$ be the joint probability function for a pair of stochastic variables x and y, defined over a discrete set, and let

$$f(x) = \sum_y \varphi(x,y) \qquad \text{and} \qquad g(y) = \sum_x \varphi(x,y)$$

be the corresponding marginal probability functions. Then, conditional probability functions are given by

$$(a) \qquad f_{y_0}(x) = \frac{\varphi(x,y_0)}{g(y_0)}, \qquad g_{x_0}(y) = \frac{\varphi(x_0,y)}{f(x_0)}.$$

Conditional probabilities are given by

(b) $pr_{y=y_0}\{x = x_0\} = f_{y_0}(x_0) = \dfrac{\varphi(x_0,y_0)}{g(y_0)},$

$$pr_{x=x_0}\{y = y_0\} = g_{x_0}(y_0) = \dfrac{\varphi(x_0,y_0)}{f(x_0)}.$$

For another very useful description of conditional probability in the finite case, see Theorem V below.

20. The Multiplication Theorem

Definition 1 shows clearly that, if the joint density function is given, the conditional probabilities are determined. The interesting thing is that we can go the other way. If the marginal density functions and all the conditional probabilities are known, the joint density function can be found. To see how this is accomplished, we need to look at the multiplication theorem.

Theorem IV.

$$pr\{AB\} = pr\{A\}pr_A\{B\} = pr\{B\}pr_B\{A\}.$$

Note that AB and BA are the same event, represented by the same area in the xy plane. Thus, the proof of one of these equalities proves the other by an interchange of symbols. As noted in Chap. 2, we shall assume (in order to stay on the level of elementary calculus) that the component events can be represented by intervals on the x and y axes. Let A be the event $a \le x \le b$, and let B be $c \le y \le d$. Then the proof of Theorem IV is a simple computation:

$$pr\{AB\} = \int_c^d \int_a^b \varphi(x,y)dx\,dy = \int_a^b f(x)dx \int_c^d \frac{\int_a^b \varphi(x,y)dx}{\int_a^b f(x)dx} dy$$

$$= \int_a^b f(x)dx \int_c^d g_{a,b}(y)dy = pr\{A\}pr_A\{B\}.$$

If A is itself a compound event A_1A_2, then Theorem IV can be applied twice to give

$$pr\{A_1A_2B\} = pr\{A_1A_2\}pr_{A_1A_2}\{B\} = pr\{A_1\}pr_{A_1}\{A_2\}pr_{A_1A_2}\{B\}.$$

Continuing in the same manner, we get a general multiplication principle:

Corollary 1.

$$pr\{E_1E_2 \cdots E_n\} = pr\{E_1\}pr_{E_1}\{E_2\}pr_{E_1E_2}\{E_3\}$$
$$\cdots pr_{E_1E_2 \cdots E_{n-1}}\{E_n\}.$$

The multiplication theorem tells us that conditional probabilities are described by the equation

(1) $$pr_A\{B\} = \frac{pr\{AB\}}{pr\{A\}}.$$

Suppose we have a physical situation in which there are n equally likely results; suppose the event A is a set of r of these and r' of these r results are also contained in the event B. Then the event AB is just these r' results; so by Definition 1, Chap. 2,

$$pr\{A\} = \frac{r}{n},$$

$$pr\{AB\} = \frac{r'}{n};$$

and Equation (1) tells us that
$$pr_A\{B\} = \frac{r'/n}{r/n} = \frac{r'}{r}.$$

To give a formal statement:

Theorem V.   Suppose the events A and B are sets of equally likely results of an experiment.   If A is a set of r such results and if r' of these r results are also contained in B, then $pr_A\{B\} = r'/r$.

21. Bayes' Theorem

Conditional probabilities in general are described by Equation (1), Sec. 20; and problems involving conditional probabilities can frequently be solved by the direct application of this equation.   However, there is an interesting special case, known as Bayes' theorem, that is worth taking a look at.

Suppose we have a situation in which an event A can occur only in conjunction with one of the mutually exclusive events $B_1, B_2, \ldots, B_n$. Symbolically, we write this

$$A = \sum_{i=1}^{n} AB_i.$$

For a physical picture, think of the events $B_1, B_2, \ldots, B_n$ as the set of all possible causes and of A as the result.   Suppose, further, that the conditional probabilities $pr_{B_i}\{A\}$ are known.   We should like to find the reverse conditional probabilities $pr_A\{B_i\}$.

If we think of the events B_i as hypotheses or causes and of A as a final result, $pr_A\{B_i\}$ is interpreted as follows: If we know that the result is A, what is the probability that the cause of it was B_i? For this reason the probabilities given by Bayes' theorem are called a posteriori probabilities—the idea being that the probability of a possible cause is computed *after* the result has transpired. The student should note that this name is given to the conditional probability $pr_A\{B_i\}$ only because of the applications usually made of this theorem. Fundamentally, it is just another conditional probability; and as the student can see by looking at (*b*) of Definition 1, there is no essential distinction between the two ideas of conditional probability.

Noting that the compound events AB_i and B_iA are the same thing, and applying Theorem IV, we have

$$pr\{A\}pr_A\{B_i\} = pr\{AB_i\} = pr\{B_iA\} = pr\{B_i\}pr_{B_i}\{A\}.$$

Solving this for $pr_A\{B_i\}$, we have

$$pr_A\{B_i\} = \frac{pr\{B_i\}pr_{B_i}\{A\}}{pr\{A\}}.$$

From the assumptions that $A = \Sigma AB_i$ and that the events B_i are mutually exclusive, we have, by Axiom C and Theorem IV, that

$$pr\{A\} = \sum_{j=1}^{n} pr\{B_j\}pr_{B_j}\{A\}.$$

Substituting, we arrive at the formula usually known as Bayes' theorem:

$$(1) \qquad pr_A\{B_i\} = \frac{pr\{B_i\}pr_{B_i}\{A\}}{\displaystyle\sum_{j=1}^{n} pr\{B_j\}pr_{B_j}\{A\}}.$$

Before getting wild ideas about what Bayes' theorem can do for us, we should look carefully at the right-hand side of (1). The important thing we see there is that, in order to compute $pr_A\{B_i\}$, we have to know *all* the a priori probabilities $pr\{B_j\}$. For instance, we might ask the question: "Knowing that a sample came from one of a given set of populations, can we tell by looking at the sample the probability that it came from a certain one?" Let us note that before we can use Bayes' theorem to answer this, we must first answer the question: "Can we tell without looking at the sample the probability that it came from a certain population?" In many cases intelligent assumptions as to the a priori probabilities can be made, but we should note that we do not get something for nothing here.   We still have to start with an assumption, and all our results are based on that assumption.

22. Construction of Joint Density Functions

The notion of conditional probability furnishes us with the necessary tools for the construction of joint density functions to represent given physical situations.

Theorem VI (*Working Rule*).   If a situation involves events each of which is to be regarded as the product of two events, then to get a stochastic variable representation:

(*a*) Classify the component events into two classes X and Y such that every compound event involved is the product of one event of class X and one of class Y.

(*b*) Represent the events of class X by a single stochastic variable x, and find the density function (or probability function).   Use Theorem III or V, Chap. 2, whichever applies.

(*c*) Associate the events of class Y in some natural manner with values of a variable y.

(*d*) *Discrete Case.*   For each value x_0 of x, get $pr\{x = x_0\}$ from the probability function in (*b*).   Then, for each value y_0 of y, figure out from the physical situation $pr_{x=x_0}\{y = y_0\}$.   Put these results into Theorem IV, and get $pr\{x = x_0 \text{ and } y = y_0\}$.   Use this as the value of $\varphi(x_0, y_0)$.

(*d'*) *Continuous Case.*   For each value x_0 of x, set up the usual approximation $pr\{x_0 \leq x \leq x_0 + dx\} = f(x_0)dx$ from the density function in (*b*).   Then, for each value y_0 of y, figure out from the physical situation the usual type of approximation to the conditional probability $pr_{x_0 \leq x \leq x_0 + dx}\{y_0 \leq y \leq y_0 + dy\}$.   Use these results and Theorem IV to get an approximation to $pr\{x_0 \leq x \leq x_0 + dx \text{ and } y_0 \leq y \leq y_0 + dy\}$.   Express this final result in the form $\varphi(x_0, y_0)dx\,dy$, and this gives the form of the joint density function φ.

We omit all proof that this rule does what it is advertised as doing.   In the discrete case this follows at once from (*d*) of Theorem II.   In the continuous case we meet with the same difficulties that caused us to skip the proof of Theorem V, Chap. 2.

In Step (*a*) the question of which set of component events to call X and which to call Y is decided by looking ahead to (*d*) or (*d'*) and seeing which set of conditional probabilities can be computed readily.   After a little experience the student will find that in some cases it makes no difference, while in others the problem is easy one way but practically impossible the other.

For many situations Theorem VI is unnecessarily complicated, and we do not want to be quoted as recommending an unduly laborious presentation for every problem the student works. We have merely tried to give full and explicit instructions for the benefit of anyone who is having trouble. Here is a short summary of this working rule that may prove more useful than the formal rule itself. If a set of events can be arranged naturally in a two-dimensional array, arrange them that way and assign abscissas and ordinates. The joint probability function will be given in the discrete case by the probabilities of the various points in the array. The form of the joint density function will be indicated in the continuous case by the probability of a representative square dx by dy. Compute these probabilities by any means that come to hand. Theorem IV will frequently be of use in this connection.

23. Independent Stochastic Variables

Before turning to specific examples, we should introduce the notion of *independent stochastic variables*. A common-sense definition of this notion would be that x and y are independent if probabilities for y do not depend on values of x. Stated in terms of the notation we are using in this chapter, this would mean that $g_{a,b}(y)$ does not depend on a or b. If this is the case, we get the same result for every a and b; so setting $a = -\infty$, $b = \infty$, we have

$$g_{a,b}(y) = \frac{\int_a^b \varphi(x,y)dx}{\int_a^b f(x)dx} = \frac{\int_{-\infty}^\infty \varphi(x,y)dx}{\int_{-\infty}^\infty f(x)dx} = \frac{g(y)}{1}$$

for every a, b. Thus for independent variables

$$\int_a^b \varphi(x,y)dx = g(y) \int_a^b f(x)dx;$$

and, integrating with respect to y, we have

$$\int_c^d \int_a^b \varphi(x,y)dx\, dy = \int_c^d g(y)dy \int_a^b f(x)dx,$$

which means Theorem IV will read $pr\{AB\} = pr\{A\}pr\{B\}$. Furthermore, since the above must hold for every a, b, c, d, it follows that $\varphi(x,y) = f(x)g(y)$. This is another of those things which we have no intention of trying to prove in an elementary course, but we can generate a strong suspicion that it would be the case by letting $a = x_0$, $b = x_0 + dx$, $c = y_0$, and $d = y_0 + dy$:

$$\int_{x_0}^{x_0+dx} \int_{y_0}^{y_0+dy} \varphi(x,y)dy\ dx = \int_{x_0}^{x_0+dx} f(x)dx \int_{y_0}^{y_0+dy} g(y)dy.$$

Now, we make our usual approximation and have

$$\varphi(x_0,y_0)dy\ dx = f(x_0)dx\ g(y_0)dy;$$

and, dividing by $dy\ dx$, we get $\varphi(x_0,y_0) = f(x_0)g(y_0)$. It is the use of the approximation that keeps this argument from being rigorous. For the benefit of those who are interested, we might add that a genuine proof would consist in applying the first mean value theorem for integrals (Franklin, *Treatise on Advanced Calculus*, page 201) to get the result in case the functions are continuous and then noting that integrability will require continuity at so many points that we can change things to make the result hold everywhere without altering the value of any integrals.

Finally, let us note that it is trivial to go back from this last result to our starting point; *i.e.*, if $\varphi(x,y) = f(x)g(y)$, then $g_{a,b}(y)$ is independent of a and b; for, in this case,

$$g_{a,b}(y) = \frac{\int_a^b \varphi(x,y)dx}{\int_a^b f(x)dx} = \frac{\int_a^b f(x)g(y)dx}{\int_a^b f(x)dx} = \frac{g(y)\int_a^b f(x)dx}{\int_a^b f(x)dx} = g(y).$$

A similar circle of implications could be given, starting with the proposition that $f_{c,d}(x)$ is independent of c and d. Thus we have four equivalent statements which we use to define independent stochastic variables.

Definition 2. The stochastic variables x and y are said to be independent if the following four equivalent conditions hold:

(a) $\qquad\qquad g_{a,b}(y) = g(y)$ for every a, b.

(b) $\qquad\qquad f_{c,d}(x) = f(x)$ for every c, d.

(c) $pr\{a \le x \le b$ and $c \le y \le d\}$
$\qquad\qquad = pr\{a \le x \le b\}pr\{c \le y \le d\}$ for every a, b, c, d.

(d) $\qquad\qquad \varphi(x,y) = f(x)g(y)$ for every x, y.

For practical purposes, note that this equivalence means that to prove x and y are independent we need prove only that some one of these conditions holds, while if x and y are known to be independent, then it follows that all four conditions hold.

The phrase "independent events" is frequently used in probability theory. We shall say that two events are independent if they can be described, one by a set of x values and the other by a set of y values, where x and y are independent stochastic variables. Conditions (a), (b), and (c) of Definition 2 then translate immediately:

Theorem VII.   For independent events A and B,

(a) $\qquad\qquad\qquad\qquad pr_A\{B\} = pr\{B\}.$

(b) $\qquad\qquad\qquad\qquad pr_B\{A\} = pr\{A\}.$

(c) $\qquad\qquad\qquad\qquad pr\{AB\} = pr\{A\}pr\{B\}.$

Furthermore, any one of these conditions will guarantee that A and B are independent.

Generalizing condition (d) of Definition 2 for independent stochastic variables, we say that n stochastic variables are independent if their joint density function is the product of n functions each depending on only 1 of the variables.   If n variables are independent, any 2 of them are; but the converse is not true.   Consider 3 variables x, y, and z, each of which assumes the values 0 and 1.   The joint probability function $\Phi(x,y,z)$ must then be defined at each corner of the unit cube; let it be defined by the numbers at the corners of the cube in this diagram:

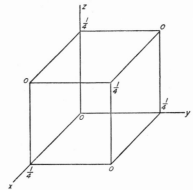

Fɪɢ. 5.

Now, to get $\varphi(x,y)$, we add along each line parallel to the z axis and discover that $\varphi(x,y)$ is $\frac{1}{4}$ at each of its 4 points.   Similarly, adding with respect to y and z, respectively, we find that $\theta(x,z)$ and $\psi(y,z)$ are each identically $\frac{1}{4}$.   From these squares with $\frac{1}{4}$ at each corner, it is easy to see that another round of adding gives $f(x) = \frac{1}{2}$ at each of its two points and the same for $g(y)$ and $h(z)$.   When we try to build back up by multiplication, we see that $f(x)g(y) = \frac{1}{2} \times \frac{1}{2} = \frac{1}{4} = \varphi(x,y)$ for each of the 4 pairs of values of x and y.   Similarly, $\theta(x,z) = f(x)h(z)$ at all 4 points in the xz plane, and $\psi(y,z) = g(y)h(z)$ at all 4 points. However, $f(x)g(y)h(z)$ is identically equal to $\frac{1}{8}$, and $\Phi(x,y,z)$ is not equal to $\frac{1}{8}$ anywhere.   Thus, x and y are independent; x and z are independent; y and z are independent; but x, y, and z are not.

24. Joint Density Functions—Independent Case

If, in setting up a two-dimensional stochastic variable representation of a situation, we find that the events we have represented by y values are independent of those represented by x values (and the physical situation will usually show very clearly that this is or is not the case), then we shall want to make x and y independent stochastic variables; and the problem of setting up the joint density function is considerably simplified. Technically, Theorem VI still applies; but practically it is far too complicated. In its place we suggest the following:

Theorem VIII (*Special Working Rule*). Follow through steps (a), (b), and (c) of Theorem VI; then, if x and y appear to be independent, set up $g(y)$ by means of Theorem III or V, Chap. 2 (whichever applies), multiply by the $f(x)$ obtained in (b) of Theorem VI, and use this product for $\varphi(x,y)$.

It is worth noting that, if x and y are independent and each has a constant density function, then $\varphi(x,y)$ will be constant also. The continuous case is particularly worth studying under these circumstances. If φ is constant, then $\varphi(x,y) = 1/A$, where A is the total area covered by all possible results. With $\varphi(x,y)$ identically $1/A$, the integral of φ over any area A' inside this just gives A'/A. These observations suggest the following:

Theorem IX (*Very Special Working Rule*). In the continuous case, for two independent stochastic variables, each with a constant density function, the probability of an event described by pairs of values of x and y is given by the area representing the favorable cases divided by the area representing all possible cases.

Many problems fall under this rule, and for these problems the solution is certainly very simple. Care must be taken, however, not to use Theorem IX where it does not apply; and the most likely source of trouble is that x and y can have constant density functions and still not come under Theorem IX. Independence must be checked in addition to this. Consider, for example, a joint density function

$$\varphi(x,y) = \begin{cases} \dfrac{1}{4\pi^2}\,(1 - \sin x \sin y) & \text{for } 0 \le x \le 2\pi \text{ and } 0 \le y \le 2\pi, \\ 0 & \text{otherwise.} \end{cases}$$

Obviously, probabilities are not proportional to areas in this case; yet the marginal density functions are both constant.

25. Example—Three Urns

Suppose we have three urns containing balls as follows:

Urn I: 3 white, 2 black
Urn II: 4 white, 7 black
Urn III: 5 white, 4 black

Our procedure will be to choose an urn at random and then draw a ball from it.   Two specific questions that might be raised are: (a) What is the probability that the ball drawn is white?   (b) Given that the ball drawn is white, what is the probability that the urn chosen was urn I? Finally, we might set up a complete representation of this situation by two stochastic variables.

To answer question (a), we note that a white ball can be obtained in any one of three mutually exclusive ways:

Urn I, white ball
Urn II, white ball
Urn III, white ball

Each of these is a compound event, but their probabilities can be computed from Theorem IV because the conditional probability for a color, given the urn number, is obvious.   So we have

$$pr\{\mathrm{I},w\} = pr\{\mathrm{I}\}pr_\mathrm{I}\{w\} = \tfrac{1}{3} \times \tfrac{3}{5} = \tfrac{1}{5}.$$
$$pr\{\mathrm{II},w\} = pr\{\mathrm{II}\}pr_\mathrm{II}\{w\} = \tfrac{1}{3} \times \tfrac{4}{11} = \tfrac{4}{33}.$$
$$pr\{\mathrm{III},w\} = pr\{\mathrm{III}\}pr_\mathrm{III}\{w\} = \tfrac{1}{3} \times \tfrac{5}{9} = \tfrac{5}{27}.$$

Applying Axiom C, we get

$$pr\{w\} = \frac{1}{5} + \frac{4}{33} + \frac{5}{27} = \frac{752}{1{,}485}.$$

Question (b) calls for a direct application of Bayes' theorem, Equation (1), Sec. 21:

$$pr_w\{\mathrm{I}\} = \frac{pr\{\mathrm{I}\}pr_\mathrm{I}\{w\}}{pr\{\mathrm{I}\}pr_\mathrm{I}\{w\} + pr\{\mathrm{II}\}pr_\mathrm{II}\{w\} + pr\{\mathrm{III}\}pr_\mathrm{III}\{w\}}$$
$$= \frac{\tfrac{1}{3} \times \tfrac{3}{5}}{\tfrac{1}{3} \times \tfrac{3}{5} + \tfrac{1}{3} \times \tfrac{4}{11} + \tfrac{1}{3} \times \tfrac{5}{9}}$$
$$= {}^{297}\!/_{752}.$$

To get a stochastic variable representation of this situation, we note that each event under consideration is characterized by an urn and a color. So, we let x represent the urn chosen and y the color drawn. We found half the values of $\varphi(x,y)$ in answering question (a). The others are found in a similar manner, and the complete picture (including marginal probability functions) looks like this:

y	$g(y)$			
b	$\dfrac{733}{1,485}$	$\dfrac{2}{15}$	$\dfrac{7}{33}$	$\dfrac{4}{27}$
w	$\dfrac{752}{1,485}$	$\dfrac{1}{5}$	$\dfrac{4}{33}$	$\dfrac{5}{27}$
		$\dfrac{1}{3}$	$\dfrac{1}{3}$	$\dfrac{1}{3}$	$f(x)$
		I	II	III	x

26. Example—Points Chosen at Random

Suppose two points are chosen independently and at random between 0 and 1. For a stochastic variable representation, we let x be the position of one of the points and y the position of the other. Then each point in the unit square of the xy plane represents a way of choosing the two points between 0 and 1. With x and y chosen independently and at random, we see that Theorem IX applies. Even that rule is simplified here because the total area is unity. So, to find the probability of an event, we must find its representation in the xy plane and get the area of that representation.

For instance, suppose we want the probability that the two points chosen between 0 and 1 are within ϵ of each other. Analytically, this would be written $|x - y| \leq \epsilon$, and geometrically it is represented by the diagonal strip:

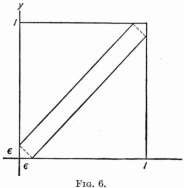

FIG. 6.

The strip consists (as shown) of a rectangle $\sqrt{2} - (2\epsilon/\sqrt{2})$ by $\epsilon\sqrt{2}$ and two triangles, each with base ϵ and altitude ϵ; therefore

$$pr\{|x - y| \le \epsilon\} = \epsilon\sqrt{2}\left(\sqrt{2} - 2\frac{\epsilon}{\sqrt{2}}\right) + 2\frac{\epsilon^2}{2} = 2\epsilon - \epsilon^2.$$

Let us modify the problem so as to make the variables dependent. Suppose the first point is chosen at random between 0 and 1 and then the second point is chosen at random to the left of it. We let x and y have the same significance as before, note that $f(x)$ is unity from 0 to 1 and zero elsewhere, and proceed to (d') of Theorem VI. If $x = x_0$, then y is chosen at random on a segment of length x_0; so

$$pr_{x=x_0}\{y_0 \le y \le y_0 + dy\} = \begin{cases} \dfrac{dy}{x_0} & \text{for } 0 \le y_0 \le x_0, \\ 0 & \text{otherwise.} \end{cases}$$

Now, since $f(x) = 1$ for $0 \le x \le 1$,

$$pr\{x_0 \le x \le x_0 + dx\} = \begin{cases} dx & \text{for } 0 \le x_0 \le 1, \\ 0 & \text{otherwise.} \end{cases}$$

So, using Theorem IV, we have

$$pr\{x_0 \le x \le x_0 + dx \text{ and } y_0 \le y \le y_0 + dy\}$$
$$\simeq \begin{cases} \dfrac{dx\,dy}{x_0} & \text{for } 0 \le y_0 \le x_0, \, 0 \le x_0 \le 1, \\ 0 & \text{otherwise.} \end{cases}$$

Therefore, $\varphi(x,y) = 1/x$ inside the triangle $0 \le y \le x, 0 \le x \le 1$ and is zero elsewhere.

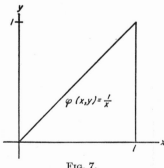

We should note in passing that, even though $1/x$ is the product of a function of x alone $(1/x)$ and a function of y alone (identically 1), $\varphi(x,y)$ is no such thing. This is because the formula $\varphi = 1/x$ applies only in a triangle. So (d) of Definition 2 does not apply. These variables are definitely dependent. This appears very clearly if we compute the marginal density functions:

Fig. 7.

$$f(x) = \int_{-\infty}^{\infty} \varphi(x,y)dy = \int_0^x \frac{1}{x}dy = 1;$$
$$g(y) = \int_{-\infty}^{\infty} \varphi(x,y)dx = \int_y^1 \frac{1}{x}dx = \log\left(\frac{1}{y}\right).$$

Obviously, $f(x)g(y)$ is different from $\varphi(x,y)$.

For this dependent case the probability that the points between 0 and 1 are within ϵ of each other can no longer be found by Theorem IX, but (c) of Theorem I will do the job very nicely. Since $\varphi(x,y) = 0$ for $y > x$, we have only half the strip we had before. For purposes of setting up limits of integration, we divide our strip into two sections. Now, by (c) of Theorem I,

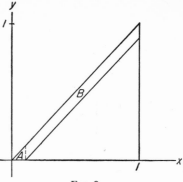

FIG. 8.

$$pr\{|x - y| \leq \epsilon\} = \int\int_A \varphi(x,y)dy\ dx + \int\int_B \varphi(x,y)dy\ dx$$

$$= \int_0^\epsilon \int_0^x \frac{1}{x}\ dy\ dx + \int_\epsilon^1 \int_{x-\epsilon}^x \frac{1}{x}\ dy\ dx$$

$$= \epsilon\left(1 + \log\frac{1}{\epsilon}\right).$$

27. Example—The Buffon Needle Problem

Another illustration that fits Theorem IX is the Buffon needle problem. A board is ruled with equidistant parallel lines, the distance between consecutive lines being d. A needle of length $a < d$ is thrown on the board. What is the probability that the needle will intersect one of the lines? Let us consider the relation of the needle to the line it touches or the nearest line below it. We shall characterize its position by means of the variables y and θ. We now assume that y and θ

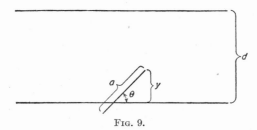

FIG. 9.

have constant density functions and are independent. The possible cases are described by the conditions $0 \leq \theta \leq \pi$, $0 \leq y \leq d$; the favorable cases, by $0 \leq y \leq a\sin\theta$. By Theorem IX, the required probability is equal to the shaded area divided by the total area:

$$p = \frac{\int_0^\pi a \sin \theta \, d\theta}{\pi d} = \frac{2a}{\pi d}.$$

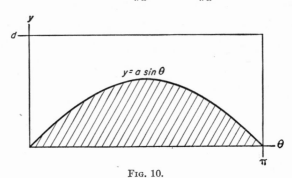

FIG. 10.

This problem was first mentioned in print by Buffon in 1733 and attracted attention for years after that. Its chief fascination lay in the fact that the number π appears in the answer. The idea was that from the result $p = 2a/\pi d$ one could get the "formula" $\pi = 2a/pd$; then an experimental evaluation of p would lead to a simple "computation of π." Uspensky (*Introduction to Mathematical Probability*, pages 112 to 113) cites the results of several such experiments in which the answers are quite reasonable. However, these can hardly be regarded as verification that $\pi = 3.14159 \ldots$. Instead, they serve as evidence that we were correct in assuming that y and θ are independent variables, each with a constant density function.

28. Example—Genetics

So far our illustrative examples have been concerned chiefly with the use of stochastic variables in connection with probability problems. We have emphasized this approach because the stochastic variable furnishes the framework for most of our later discussion. It should be pointed out, however, that the addition principle (Axiom *C*) and the multiplication theorem (Theorem IV) may be used quite effectively in the solution of many simple problems concerning probabilities, with no recourse to the notion of a stochastic variable at all.

A good example of this procedure is furnished by a simple problem from the field of genetics. Each organism has certain characteristics (color in plants, eye color in human beings, etc.) determined by genes. For each such characteristic, the organism has two genes, each of which is of one of two kinds. The genes are usually designated by A and a; thus the possible gene types are AA, Aa, and aa. In the process

of reproduction, the offspring inherits one gene from each parent. If
the parent is of type AA or aa, the inherited gene must be A or a,
respectively. An Aa parent may transmit either kind of gene with
probability $\frac{1}{2}$.

Suppose, now, that we have a population (called the zero generation)
with the genes so distributed that if a member is chosen at random, the
probabilities of the various gene types are:

AA	Aa	aa
p	$2q$	r

If parents are chosen independently and at random from this population, what are the probabilities for the various possible gene types in
the next generation?

Each result in the first generation is the product of four independent
factors: the gene type of each parent and the choice of a gene from each
of these. We shall designate such a result by listing the type of one
parent, the gene transmitted, the type of the other parent, and the gene
transmitted. For instance, $AA, A; Aa, a$ will mean that one parent
was of type AA and (necessarily) transmitted an A gene, while the
other was of type Aa and transmitted an a gene. Because of the
assumed independence of these four events, we can use (c) of Theorem
VII to get the probability of such a fourfold event.

The type AA in the first generation can result in any of the following
mutually exclusive ways:

Result	Intermediate steps	Probability
$AA, A; AA, A$	$p \cdot 1 \cdot p \cdot 1$	p^2
$AA, A; Aa, A$	$p \cdot 1 \cdot 2q \cdot \frac{1}{2}$	pq
$Aa, A; AA, A$	$2q \cdot \frac{1}{2} \cdot p \cdot 1$	pq
$Aa, A; Aa, A$	$2q \cdot \frac{1}{2} \cdot 2q \cdot \frac{1}{2}$	q^2

Thus, by Axiom C, the probability of AA in the first generation is

$$p^2 + 2pq + q^2 = (p + q)^2.$$

To get Aa in the first generation, we have the following mutually
exclusive possibilities:

Result	Intermediate steps	Probability
$AA, A; aa, a$	$p \cdot 1 \cdot r \cdot 1$	pr
$AA, A; Aa, a$	$p \cdot 1 \cdot 2q \cdot \frac{1}{2}$	pq
$Aa, A; aa, a$	$2q \cdot \frac{1}{2} \cdot r \cdot 1$	qr
$Aa, A; Aa, a$	$2q \cdot \frac{1}{2} \cdot 2q \cdot \frac{1}{2}$	q^2

There is a symmetric set of results yielding aA (which amounts to the same thing); so the probability of Aa is

$$2(pr + pq + qr + q^2) = 2(p + q)(q + r).$$

By symmetry, the probability of aa is

$$(q + r)^2,$$

so we have the following table for the first generation:

AA	Aa	aa
$(p + q)^2$	$2(p + q)(q + r)$	$(q + r)^2$

Using this table, we can now study the second generation. However, there is no point in working the problem over again. Instead, let

$$P = (p + q)^2,$$
$$Q = (p + q)(q + r),$$
$$R = (q + r)^2.$$

Then use the previous results. Now, if we remember that because of their original significance, $p + 2q + r = 1$, we find that

$$(P + Q)^2 = (p + q)^2(p + 2q + r)^2 = (p + q)^2,$$
$$(P + Q)(Q + R) = (p + q)(p + 2q + r)(q + r)(p + 2q + r)$$
$$= (p + q)(q + r),$$
$$(Q + R)^2 = (q + r)^2(p + 2q + r)^2 = (q + r)^2.$$

That is, the probabilities for the second generation are the same as those for the first. Thus, no matter what the distribution in the zero generation, the probability distribution is stable from the first generation on.

The student should note carefully that these are all a priori probabilities—computed on the basis of an assumption about the zero generation only. If the population is very large, we can show (see Chap. 11) that there is a large probability that any given generation will show an actual distribution close to that indicated by the a priori probability distribution. However, it is stretching things too far to say that they should all be close. Therefore, even though we have proved the stability of the a priori probabilities, it does not follow that the actual distribution will (even probably) be stable at all. The question of the probability of stability for the actual distributions is a very complicated one that we shall not attempt to answer.

REFERENCES FOR FURTHER STUDY

Coolidge, *An Introduction to Mathematical Probability*, Chap. II.
Levy and Roth, *Elements of Probability*, Chaps. IV, VI.
Uspensky, *Introduction to Mathematical Probability*, Chaps. II, XII.

PROBLEMS

1. What is the probability that each of the 4 players in a bridge game will be dealt a complete suit of cards?   *Ans.* $4!(13!)^4/52!$.

2. Each of two urns contains 5 white and 7 black balls. One ball is drawn from each urn. What is the probability that both balls drawn are white?   *Ans.* $25/144$.

3. The urns of Prob. 2 are emptied into a third urn, and 2 balls are drawn simultaneously from this third urn. What is the probability that both balls drawn are white?   *Ans.* $15/92$.

4. Three urns contain, respectively, 2 white and 3 black balls, 4 white and 2 black balls, 3 white and 1 black balls. One ball is drawn from each urn. What is the probability that among the balls drawn there are 2 white and 1 black? Represent this problem by three stochastic variables, and draw a picture.   *Ans.* $14/30$.

5. Two urns contain, respectively, 4 white and 3 black balls, 3 white and 7 black balls. One urn is selected and a ball drawn from it. What is the probability that this ball is white?   *Ans.* $61/140$.

6. Represent Prob. 5 by two stochastic variables; describe the joint density function, and answer the following question: Given that the ball was white, what is the probability that the urn chosen was the first one?   *Ans.* $40/61$.

7. Urns A and B contain, respectively, 2 white and 1 black balls, 1 white and 5 black balls. One ball is transferred from A to B, and then one ball is drawn from B. What is the probability that this ball drawn from B will be white?   *Ans.* $5/21$.

8. Represent Prob. 7 by a pair of stochastic variables. Set up the joint density function, and answer the following question: If the ball drawn from B was white, what is the probability that the ball transferred from A to B was also white?   *Ans.* $4/5$.

9. Three urns contain, respectively, 2 white and 3 black balls, 1 white and 5 black balls, 6 white and 2 black balls. An urn is chosen at random and a ball drawn from it. If the ball drawn is white, what is the probability that the urn was the third one?   *Ans.* $45/79$.

10. Two urns contain, respectively, 1 white and 1 black ball, 2 white and no black balls. One urn is selected at random. A ball is drawn and replaced; then another drawing is made from the same urn.   Each draw yields a white ball.   What is the probability that the urn selected was the second one?   *Ans.* $\frac{4}{5}$.

11. The same as Prob. 10, but 3 drawings were made, each yielding a white ball.   *Ans.* $\frac{8}{9}$.

12. An urn contains 10 white and 10 black balls.   Five balls are transferred to another urn, and samples are drawn from this second urn, one at a time, with replacements.   If 5 such independent samples are all white, what is the probability that the second urn contains only white balls?   Hint: See Prob. 21, Chap. 2.

Ans. $\frac{21}{118}$.

13. In a sequence of throws with 2 dice, what is the probability of throwing a 7 for the first time on the nth throw?   *Ans.* $\frac{1}{6}(\frac{5}{6})^{n-1}$.

14. Show that the probability is 1 that a 7 will be thrown some time in an indefinite sequence of throws of 2 dice.

15. What is the probability that the first 6 will precede the first 7 in a sequence of throws with 2 dice?   *Ans.* $\frac{5}{11}$.

16. The game of craps is played as follows: A man throws 2 dice. If, on his first throw, he gets either 7 or 11, he wins the game.   If, on his first throw, he gets 2, 3, or 12, he loses.   If, on his first throw, he gets 4, 5, 6, 8, 9, or 10, he continues to throw the dice until he either duplicates the total obtained on his first throw or throws a 7.   If the total on this final throw duplicates his first total, he wins.   If the final throw is a 7, he loses.   What is the probability that the man with the dice will win?   *Ans.* $\frac{244}{495}$.

17. Take Definition 1, Chap. 2, as a definition of probability and Theorem V of this chapter as a definition of conditional probability, and prove the multiplication theorem (Theorem IV).

18. An urn contains n balls, numbered 1, 2, . . . , n.   Two balls are drawn one after the other, without replacement.   Let x be the number on the first ball and y the number on the second.   Set up the joint probability function for x and y, and show that the marginal probability functions are the same.

19. Generalize Prob. 18.   If all the balls are removed, one after the other, the probability function for the number on any given draw is the same as for any other draw.

20. Show that in Prob. 19 all permutations of the numbers 1, 2, · . . , n are equally likely.

21. Two points are chosen at random on a line segment.   What is the probability that the 3 segments determined can form the sides of a triangle?   *Ans.* $\frac{1}{4}$.

22. The same as Prob. 21, except that one point is chosen at random; then the other is chosen at random to the right of it.

Ans. $-\tfrac{1}{2} + \log 2$.

23. Given the joint density function

$$\varphi(x,y) = \begin{cases} 3x^2y + 3y^2x & \text{for } 0 \le x \le 1 \text{ and } 0 \le y \le 1, \\ 0 & \text{otherwise,} \end{cases}$$

find the conditional probability $pr_{\frac{1}{2} \le x \le \frac{3}{4}}\{\tfrac{1}{3} \le y \le \tfrac{2}{3}\}$. *Ans.* $^{311}\!/_{1053}$.

24. Find the marginal density functions in Prob. 23.

Ans. $x + \tfrac{3}{2}x^2$, $y + \tfrac{3}{2}y^2$.

25. Are the stochastic variables in Prob. 23 dependent or independent? Why?

In each of Probs. 26 to 31, a joint density (or probability) function $\varphi(x,y)$ is described. It is understood that $\varphi(x,y) = 0$ outside the region specified. In each case apply (d) of Definition 2 to determine whether the variables are dependent or independent.

26. $\varphi(x,y) = (1/4\pi^2)[1 - \sin(x + y)]$ $(-\pi \le x \le \pi, -\pi \le y \le \pi)$.

Ans. dep.

27. $\varphi(x,y) = \dfrac{1}{2}[\cos(x + y) + \cos(x - y)]$ $\left(0 \le x \le \dfrac{\pi}{2}, 0 \le y \le \dfrac{\pi}{2}\right)$.

Ans. ind.

28. $\varphi(x,y) = 4xy$ $(0 \le x \le 1, 0 \le y \le 1)$. *Ans.* ind.

29. $\varphi(x,y) = 8xy$ $(0 \le x \le y, 0 \le y \le 1)$. *Ans.* dep.

30. $x = 1, 2, 3; y = 1, 2, 3; \varphi(x,y)$:

$\tfrac{1}{72}$	$\tfrac{1}{36}$	$\tfrac{5}{72}$
$\tfrac{1}{36}$	$\tfrac{1}{18}$	$\tfrac{5}{36}$
$\tfrac{1}{12}$	$\tfrac{1}{6}$	$\tfrac{5}{12}$

Ans. ind.

31. $x = 1, 2, 3; y = 1, 2, 3; \varphi(x,y)$:

$\tfrac{1}{10}$	$\tfrac{1}{10}$	$\tfrac{1}{10}$
$\tfrac{1}{10}$	$\tfrac{1}{5}$	$\tfrac{1}{10}$
$\tfrac{1}{10}$	$\tfrac{1}{10}$	$\tfrac{1}{10}$

Ans. dep.

32. Let $\Phi(x,y,z) = (1/8\pi^3)(1 - \sin x \sin y \sin z)$ in the cube $0 \le x \le 2\pi$, $0 \le y \le 2\pi$, $0 \le z \le 2\pi$ $(\Phi = 0$ elsewhere) be the joint density function for the three stochastic variables x, y, and z. Show that x and y are independent, y and z are independent, x and z are independent, but x, y, and z are not.

33. A number is chosen at random between 0 and 1. Let $x_n = 1$ if the nth decimal place is a 7, and let $x_n = 0$ if the nth decimal place is anything else.   Show that the stochastic variables $x_1, x_2, \ldots, x_k$ are totally independent.   Use Prob. 34, Chap. 2.   Note that to anticipate and solve Prob. 34, Chap. 2, by using (c) of Definition 2 in this chapter would be to assume the independence of these variables.

34. A number is chosen at random between 0 and 1.   Let x_n be the nth decimal place.   Show that the stochastic variables $x_1, x_2, \ldots, x_k$ are totally independent.

The A gene is dominant, the a recessive.   This means that organisms of types AA and Aa will exhibit the same physical characteristic—that going with the A gene.   Only type aa will exhibit the a characteristic, though type Aa can transmit it to offspring.   In Probs. 35 to 40, assume that the a priori probabilities for the various gene types are

$$AA \qquad Aa \qquad aa$$
$$\tfrac{1}{4} \qquad \tfrac{1}{2} \qquad \tfrac{1}{4}$$

35. If both parents have the dominant characteristic, what is the probability that the offspring will have the recessive one?   *Ans.* $\tfrac{1}{9}$.

36. If one parent has the dominant characteristic and one the recessive, what is the probability that the offspring will have the recessive one?   *Ans.* $\tfrac{1}{3}$.

37. If the offspring has the recessive characteristic, what is the probability that both parents do?   *Ans.* $\tfrac{1}{4}$.

38. If the offspring has the dominant characteristic, what is the probability that both parents do?   *Ans.* $\tfrac{2}{3}$.

39. If all four grandparents have the dominant characteristic, what is the probability that the second-generation offspring will?   *Ans.* $\tfrac{8}{9}$.

40. If all four grandparents and both parents have the dominant characteristic, what is the probability that the second-generation offspring will?   *Ans.* $\tfrac{15}{16}$.

CHAPTER 4

REPEATED TRIALS AND ALTERNATIVE EVENTS

We group together in this chapter the discussion of two rather unrelated formulas. The first amounts to no more than a special example of the combined use of the addition principle and the multiplication theorem. However, it has assumed sufficient importance in the study of probability to deserve special mention. The second formula gives us something akin to an addition principle for events which are not mutually exclusive.

29. Bernoulli Formula—Physical Version

For our first problem the physical picture is that of a sequence of experiments. In particular, we want to consider a sequence of independent but identical experiments. The first extensive study of such a situation was made by Jakob Bernoulli and published posthumously (1713). As a result, his name is usually attached to sequences of this type (Definition 1) and to the formula (Theorem I) that applies to such situations.

Definition 1. A Bernoullian sequence of trials is defined as a (finite or infinite) sequence of experiments satisfying the following conditions:

(a) For each experiment, the possible results are classified as either success or failure.

(b) The probability of success is the same for every experiment.

(c) Each result is independent of all the others.

In succeeding chapters we shall have a great deal to say about Bernoullian trials. It will facilitate matters if we adopt a standard notation in connection with them. The probability of success on an individual trial we shall always denote by p. The probability of failure $(1 - p)$ we shall denote by q.

The phrase "sequence of trials" gives the impression of a sequence of repetitions of the same experiment. Obviously, such a sequence of repetitions is an example of a Bernoullian sequence, but it is not the

61

only one by any means. For example, the simultaneous performance of the same experiment on different sets of apparatus can be an equally good example. We want to think of the "trials" as sequentially ordered, but this ordering may be purely arbitrary. It need not have anything to do with time. If we toss a single coin n times or throw a single die n times, we have an example of a Bernoullian sequence; but we also get an example by tossing n coins or throwing n dice.

It is not even necessary that we do n things to get an example of a Bernoullian sequence. If we choose a single number at random between 0 and 1, we define an infinite sequence of decimal places each of which either is a 7 (success) or is not (failure). These events are totally independent and have equal probabilities of success (Prob. 33, Chap. 3); so with one twist of the wrist we describe an infinite Bernoullian sequence.

The simplest cases of sampling furnish interesting examples of Bernoullian sequences. If an urn contains black and white balls, sample drawings (with replacement) are independent events, each with only two possible outcomes and with identical probabilities. Therefore, a single sample aggregate of this sort may be regarded as a Bernoullian sequence.

Another type of sampling that is essentially Bernoullian is a spot-check inspection on a production line. A factory is turning out gadgets of some sort. All are produced under essentially the same conditions, but occasionally a defective product will appear. Apparently there is some fixed probability (characteristic of the factory) that a given item will be defective. Furthermore, the fact that a given product is defective has no discernible effect on the probability of defects in any other products. Therefore, a single item taken off the production line and inspected furnishes us with a single "trial," and a series of such inspections forms a Bernoullian sequence.

Something else we might note is that a sequence of Bernoullian sequences may occasionally be regarded as a Bernoullian sequence. Suppose we find by the methods of this chapter (or by more efficient methods, developed later) that there is a certain probability p that a sample of 100 items off a given production line will contain exactly 2 defective items. Then, 20,000 samples, divided into 200 sets of 100 each, form an example of a Bernoullian sequence of 200 trials. Each "trial" is a set of 100 sample items. "Success" means 2 defective items out of the 100.

As a general rule, in the study of a sequence of sample sets, we are interested in more than a single question to be answered yes or no; so

the situation is usually not strictly Bernoullian.   However, many of
our later considerations concerning sequences of stochastic variables
(Chaps. 8 to 11) may be regarded as generalizations of the notion of
Bernoullian sequences.   The student would do well to get a picture in
this simplest case of the many different types of situations that can be
analyzed as sequences of "trials."

The fundamental problem in connection with Bernoullian trials concerns the probability of a given number of successes in a given (finite)
number of trials.

Theorem I (*Bernoulli's Formula*).   The probability of exactly r
successes in n Bernoullian trials is

$$^{n}C_{r}p^{r}q^{n-r}.$$

Consider a particular sequence of n results, each either a success or a
failure:

$$S\ S\ F\ S\ F\ F\ \cdots\ F\ S.$$

The probability of each S is p, and that of each F is q.   Remembering
that the trials are independent and using (c) of Theorem VII, Chap. 3,
we have that the probability of this particular sequence is

$$ppqpqq\ \cdots\ qp = p^{r}q^{n-r}.$$

Now, "r successes" means any one of the sequences containing r
successes and $n - r$ failures.   These different sequences represent
mutually exclusive events, each with probability $p^{r}q^{n-r}$.   The number
of such sequences is clearly the number of ways of putting the S's in
different positions on the framework of n places.   Since there are r of
these S's to be placed, the number of sequences is $^{n}C_{r}$.   Therefore, by
the addition principle, Axiom C, the probability of r successes in n
trials is $^{n}C_{r}p^{r}q^{n-r}$.

From Theorem I and the addition principle, we at once derive the
following corollaries:

Corollary 1.   The probability of at least r successes in n Bernoullian
trials is

$$\sum_{s=r}^{n} {}^{n}C_{s}p^{s}q^{n-s}.$$

Corollary **2.**   The probability of at most r successes in n Bernoullian trials is

$$\sum_{s=0}^{r} {}_nC_s p^s q^{n-s}.$$

30. Bernoulli Formula—Stochastic Variable Version

In order to adapt much of the discussion in later chapters to the important special case of Bernoullian sequences of trials, we should formulate a stochastic variable description of such a sequence of experiments.   If we perform a set of n experiments, the record of all n results describes a compound event with n components—each component the result of one experiment.   Thus, we describe the whole set of experiments by an n-dimensional event space with each of the n coordinates representing one experiment.   Let us call these coordinate variables x_i $(i = 1, 2, \ldots, n)$.   Note that we are using x_i to denote a variable, not a specific value of some variable x.   The convenience of this notation will soon be obvious, and the student must overcome the habit formed in analytic geometry of using subscripts with x to denote constants.

This n-dimensional representation could describe any set of n events, but in the Bernoullian case we can be much more specific.   According to (*a*) of Definition 1, each variable x_i assumes only 2 values—one representing failure, the other success.   For each variable, let these values be 0 and 1, respectively.   Then the event space consists of the 2^n corner points of the unit "cube" in n space.

Now, (*b*) of Definition 1 tells us that each variable x_i should have a probability function $f_i(x_i)$ whose form is the same for all i's; namely,

$$
\begin{array}{ccc}
x_i\colon & 0 & 1 \\
f_i(x_i)\colon & q & p
\end{array}
$$

The independence criterion, (*c*) of Definition 1, means that the stochastic variables x_i should be independent.   The mathematical interpretation of this is that the joint probability function is the product of the marginal ones:

$$\varphi(x_1, x_2, \ldots, x_n) = \prod_{i=1}^{n} f_i(x_i).$$

To see the mathematical representation of the number of successes in n trials, all we have to do is use the right words to describe what we have already said about the stochastic variables x_i. Suppose we put it this way: The value of x_i is the number of successes on the ith trial. This is exactly what we said before; and when we state it this way, it is clear that the number of successes in a given sequence of trials is the sum of the values assumed by the x's for that particular sequence.   In symbols,

$$ r = \sum_{i=1}^{n} x_i. $$

Translated into these terms, Theorem I reads as follows:

Theorem II.   If $x_1, x_2, \ldots, x_n$ are independent stochastic variables each of which assumes the values 0 and 1 with probability q and p, respectively, then

$$ r = \sum_{i=1}^{n} x_i $$

is a stochastic variable with probability function

$$ f(r) = {}^{n}C_r p^r q^{n-r}. $$

This is merely a restatement of Theorem I and therefore follows from it.   However, a direct proof of Theorem II in terms of probability functions might help to clarify some of the concepts introduced here.

We have already noted that

$$ \varphi(x_1, x_2, \ldots, x_n) = \prod_{i=1}^{n} f_i(x_i); $$

therefore if we have a point in n space for which $\sum_{1}^{n} x_i = r$ (*i.e.*, one whose coordinates consist of r ones and $n - r$ zeros), the value of φ at that point is the product of r factors p and $n - r$ factors q. In other words, $\varphi = p^r q^{n-r}$ at each such point.   Thus, $pr\{\Sigma x_i = r\}$ is $p^r q^{n-r}$ times the number of corner points of the unit cube for which $\Sigma x_i = r$.

Perhaps the easiest way to count these corner points is to repeat the argument used in proving Theorem I, noting that the corner points on the unit cube are given by sequences of zeros and 1's.   However, the following geometric picture might prove instructive. Let us draw some skeleton "cubes."

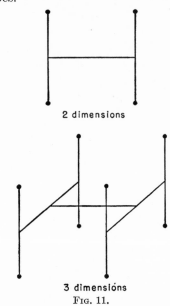

2 dimensions

3 dimensions

FIG. 11.

The hyperplanes Σx_i = constant stand out much more clearly if we collapse these cubes like this:

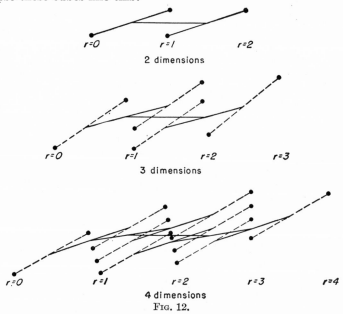

$r=0$ $r=1$ $r=2$

2 dimensions

$r=0$ $r=1$ $r=2$ $r=3$

3 dimensions

$r=0$ $r=1$ $r=2$ $r=3$ $r=4$

4 dimensions

FIG. 12.

In each of these sketches it is clear that the number of corner points for each value of r follows the formula ^nC_r. Furthermore, if we study these sketches of cubes a little more closely, we note that each one is made by taking the preceding one and drawing a line through each corner point. So, each corner point on the n cube blossoms into two on the $(n + 1)$ cube—one shifted to the left, the other to the right. Thus the corner points for a given value of r on the $(n + 1)$ cube come from those on the n cube for the values r and $r - 1$. A comparison of this remark with the identity $^{n+1}C_r = {}^nC_r + {}^nC_{r-1}$ (Prob. 18, Chap. 1) shows that the formula

$$pr\{ \Sigma x_i = r \} = {}^nC_r p^r q^{n-r}$$

must hold in general.

31. Example—Random Walk Problem

Suppose a point starts from the origin and moves along the x axis in jumps of 1 unit each. Each jump may be either forward or backward, and we shall assume that at each step the probability for each direction is $\frac{1}{2}$. Furthermore, we shall assume that each jump is independent of all the others. Aften n jumps the point might be at any one of a number of points ranging from $-n$ to n, and we want to find the probability of its being at each of the possible points in this range.

Let x_i ($i = 1, 2, \ldots, n$) be the displacement on the ith jump. Then, the x_i's are independent stochastic variables each having the probability function

$$\begin{array}{ccc} x_i: & -1 & 1 \\ f_i(x_i): & \frac{1}{2} & \frac{1}{2} \end{array}$$

Now, the net displacement (*i.e.*, the abscissa of the point) after n jumps is the sum of these n individual displacements. So, letting x be the abscissa of the point after n jumps, we have

$$x = \sum_{i=1}^{n} x_i.$$

These variables do not fit Theorem II, but the variables

$$z_i = \frac{x_i + 1}{2}$$

do fit. Therefore, from Theorem II, we have

$$pr\left\{ \sum_{i=1}^{n} z_i = r \right\} = {}^nC_r \left(\frac{1}{2}\right)^r \left(\frac{1}{2}\right)^{n-r} = \frac{{}^nC_r}{2^n}.$$

To find out about x, we note that

$$\sum_{i=1}^{n} z_i = \sum_{i=1}^{n} \frac{x_i + 1}{2} = \frac{x + n}{2}.$$

Thus, $x = a$ means $\Sigma z_i = (a + n)/2$, whence

$$pr\{x = a\} = \frac{{}^nC_{(a+n)/2}}{2^n}.$$

That is, the probability function for x is

$$f(x) = \frac{{}^nC_{(x+n)/2}}{2^n}.$$

In the two-dimensional random walk problem, we assume that at each jump the point may move 1 unit forward, backward, up, or down, each with probability $\frac{1}{4}$. Our first inclination might be to let x_i be the ith horizontal displacement and y_i the ith vertical displacement. The trouble with this is that, for each i, x_i and y_i fail to be independent because we have assumed that, if there is a horizontal displacement on a given jump, there is no vertical displacement on that jump, and vice versa.

Instead, let us tilt the x and y axes at an angle of 45° with the directions of the jumps. Then, let x_i and y_i be stochastic variables with a joint probability function $\varphi_i(x_i, y_i)$ described as follows:

y_i	$g_i(y_i)$			
1	$\frac{1}{2}$	$\frac{1}{4}$	$\frac{1}{4}$	
-1	$\frac{1}{2}$	$\frac{1}{4}$	$\frac{1}{4}$	
		$\frac{1}{2}$	$\frac{1}{2}$	$f_i(x_i)$
		-1	1	x_i

Clearly, $\varphi_i = f_i \cdot g_i$ at each point; so the variables are independent. Furthermore, they describe a random displacement of length $\sqrt{2}$ in a direction tilted at 45° to the axes. We could change scale to make the jumps of length 1, but it is much simpler to leave them the way they are.

Since the jumps are supposed to be independent of each other, this construction gives us $2n$ variables $x_1, x_2, \ldots, x_n, y_1, \ldots, y_n$, each independent of all the others. Therefore, the two sums

$$x = \sum_{i=1}^{n} x_i \qquad \text{and} \qquad y = \sum_{i=1}^{n} y_i$$

are independent of each other.   This means that the joint probability function $\varphi(x,y)$ will be the product of the two marginal probability functions $f(x)$ and $g(y)$.   These last two are exactly what we found in the one-dimensional problem; so

$$\varphi(x,y) = f(x)g(y) = \frac{{}^nC_{(x+n)/2}}{2^n} \cdot \frac{{}^nC_{(y+n)/2}}{2^n} = \frac{{}^nC_{(x+n)/2}\,{}^nC_{(y+n)/2}}{4^n}$$

gives a joint probability function for the abscissa and ordinate of the moving point after n jumps.

32. The General Addition Formula

The second problem we want to consider in this chapter is roughly this: What modifications must be made in the addition principle if the events are not mutually exclusive?   The answer to this question looks rather complicated unless we introduce some special notation.   Let $E_1, E_2, \ldots, E_n$ be any set of n events.   Then, let

$$S_1 = \sum_i pr\{E_i\}$$

$$S_2 = \sum_{i,j} pr\{E_iE_j\}$$

$$S_3 = \sum_{i,j,k} pr\{E_iE_jE_k\}$$

$$\cdots \cdots \cdots \cdots \cdots$$

$$S_n = pr\{E_1E_2 \cdots E_n\}$$

where the summations over several indices are taken to mean the sum of all terms obtained by taking combinations (not permutations) of the E_i's.   For instance, if there are three events, S_2 is

$$pr\{E_1E_2\} + pr\{E_1E_3\} + pr\{E_2E_3\},$$

not

$$pr\{E_1E_2\} + pr\{E_1E_3\} + pr\{E_2E_1\}$$
$$+ pr\{E_2E_3\} + pr\{E_3E_1\} + pr\{E_3E_2\}.$$

Theorem III.   Given any set of n events, $E_1, E_2, \ldots, E_n$,

$$pr\left\{\sum_{i=1}^n E_i\right\} = S_1 - S_2 + S_3 - \cdots \pm S_n = \sum_{k=1}^n (-1)^{k+1}S_k.$$

To prove this formula, let us think of the events E_i as point sets in an event space.   The event ΣE_i is the set of points belonging to one or more of the individual sets E_i, and $pr\{\Sigma E_i\}$ is the integral of a joint density function over this set. Each of the probabilities appearing in the sums S_k is the integral of this same density function over some set. However, the sets over which we integrate overlap. Furthermore, sometimes we add the integral, and sometimes we subtract. Let us take a collection E_{i_1}, E_{i_2}, . . . , E_{i_r} of the E's and designate by R the set of all points of ΣE_i that belong to each of these sets and to no others. Note that in general R is not the product of these sets. A point in the product might belong to other E's too. Now, each point in ΣE_i belongs to one and only one of these sets R. Therefore, we shall prove the theorem if we show that, for an arbitrary set R of this type, the right-hand side of the formula gives a net result of exactly $+1$ so far as the integral over R is concerned.

Suppose, then, that R is the set of points belonging to each of the sets E_{i_1}, E_{i_2}, . . . , E_{i_r} and to no others. A product set ΠE_i will contain the whole of R if all the subscripts over which we multiply are taken from among the indices $i_1, i_2, . . . , i_r$. Otherwise, the product set will contain none of R. So the integral over R appears in the sum S_k only if $k \leq r$, and then it appears ${}^rC_k$ times, once for every combination of k subscripts taken from the r indices associated with R. Therefore, the net count on the number of times we integrate over R is

$$\sum_{k=1}^{r} (-1)^{k+1}\, {}^rC_k.$$

Now (Prob. 20, Chap. 1),

$$0 = \sum_{k=0}^{r} (-1)^{k}\, {}^rC_k = {}^rC_0 + \sum_{k=1}^{r} (-1)^{k}\, {}^rC_k = 1 - \sum_{k=1}^{r} (-1)^{k+1}\, {}^rC_k,$$

whence

$$\sum_{k=1}^{r} (-1)^{k+1}\, {}^rC_k = 1.$$

33. Example—The Matching Problem

There is a problem with a number of applications which illustrates very nicely the use of this theorem. If n numbered balls are placed one in each of n numbered pockets, what is the probability that no one of the balls is in the pocket corresponding to its own number?

To get the answer to this, we shall compute the probability that at least one of the balls is in the right pocket and subtract the result from unity. To this end, let E_i be the event that the ith ball gets in the right pocket.   Then, the required probability is given by

$$1 - pr\left\{\sum_{i=1}^{n} E_i\right\}.$$

The second term we compute by the formula.   There are n pockets for the ith ball to go into, one of which is "right"; therefore (see Prob. 19, Chap. 3)

$$pr\{E_i\} = \frac{1}{n},$$

and

$$S_1 = \sum_i pr\{E_i\} = 1.$$

If the ith ball is in the right pocket, there are $n - 1$ pockets for the jth to choose from; so

$$pr_{E_i}\{E_j\} = \frac{1}{n - 1}.$$

Then, Theorem IV, Chap. 3, gives us that

$$pr\{E_iE_j\} = \frac{1}{n} \cdot \frac{1}{n - 1}.$$

Hence,

$$S_2 = \sum_{i,j} pr\{E_iE_j\} = \frac{^nC_2}{n(n - 1)} = \frac{1}{2!}.$$

Similarly,

$$S_3 = \sum_{i,j,k} pr\{E_iE_jE_k\} = \frac{^nC_3}{n(n - 1)(n - 2)} = \frac{1}{3!},$$

etc.   Therefore, the required probability is

$$1 - pr\left\{\sum E_i\right\} = 1 - \sum_{k=1}^{n} \frac{(-1)^{k+1}}{k!} = \sum_{k=0}^{n} \frac{(-1)^k}{k!}.$$

There are two interesting things about this probability of no correspondences.   First, it is greater for even n than for odd n.   Second, as $n \to \infty$, it tends to

$$\sum_{k=0}^{\infty} \frac{(-1)^k}{k!} = e^{-1} = .36+.$$

Using the above formula for the probability of no correspondences, we can easily find the probability of any given number of them. If a certain set of r balls is specified, the probability that each of them is in the right pocket is

$$\frac{1}{n(n - 1) \cdots (n - r + 1)}.$$

The probability that none of the others is in the right pocket is given by our original result with n replaced by $n - r$:

$$\sum_{k=0}^{n-r} \frac{(-1)^k}{k!}.$$

There are ^nC_r different sets of r balls, giving us ^nC_r mutually exclusive events of the form, "These r balls and no others are in the right pockets." The event "exactly r correspondences" is the sum of these mutually exclusive events; therefore its probability is

$$\frac{^nC_r}{n(n - 1) \cdots (n - r + 1)} \sum_{k=0}^{n-r} \frac{(-1)^k}{k!} = \frac{1}{r!} \sum_{k=0}^{n-r} \frac{(-1)^k}{k!}.$$

REFERENCES FOR FURTHER STUDY

Levy and Roth, *Elements of Probability*, Chap. V.
Uspensky, *Introduction to Mathematical Probability*, Chaps. II, III.

PROBLEMS

1. What is the probability of getting exactly 3 aces in 5 throws of a single die? at least 3 aces?   *Ans.*   250/7,776; 276/7,776.

2. What is the probability of getting at least 1 ace in 5 throws of a single die? in 4 throws?   *Ans.*   4,651/7,776; 671/1,296.

3. What is the probability of getting exactly 3 aces in a single throw of 5 dice?   *Ans.*   250/7,776.

4. A coin is tossed and the cumulative heads-tails score kept. What is the probability that the heads total will reach 6 before the tails total reaches 4?   *Ans.* $^{13}\%_{12}$.

5. Generalize Prob. 4. What is the probability of getting m heads before n tails?

$$Ans. \quad \frac{1}{2^{m+n-1}} \sum_{r=m}^{m+n-1} {}^{m+n-1}C_r.$$

6. Generalize Prob. 5. In a general sequence of Bernoullian trials (probability p of success), what is the probability of m successes before n failures?

$$Ans. \quad \sum_{r=m}^{m+n-1} {}^{m+n-1}C_r p^r q^{m+n-r-1}.$$

7. Player A has 50 cents, and player B has \$1.10. They want to play a single game in which the winner will take the entire amount. Devise an equitable game that can be played by tossing a coin. Suggestion: They toss the coin 5 times, and A bets there will be exactly 2 heads. Find at least two other simple solutions.

8. Devise an equitable coin-tossing game in which A's stake is 70 cents and B's stake is 90 cents.

9. From a supply of black and white balls 4 balls are placed in an urn, the color of each being determined by tossing a coin. A ball is drawn from the urn and replaced. This is done 4 times, and all 4 draws are white. What is the probability that the urn contains only white balls? *Ans.* $64/170$.

10. The Buffon needle experiment (see Sec. 27) is performed 5 times with the needle length one-half the distance between the lines. What is the probability that it will touch a line on 2 out of the 5 tries?

$$Ans. \quad 10\left(\frac{1}{\pi}\right)^2 \times \left(1 - \frac{1}{\pi}\right)^3.$$

11. What is the probability of throwing at least 8 exactly 4 times in 7 throws of 2 dice? *Ans.* $35(5\!/\!12)^4 \times (7\!/\!12)^3$.

12. What is the probability of throwing exactly 8 at least 4 times in 7 throws of 2 dice?

Ans. $35(5\!/\!36)^4(31\!/\!36)^3 + 21(5\!/\!36)^5(31\!/\!36)^2 + 7(5\!/\!36)^6(31\!/\!36) + (5\!/\!36)^7$.

13. There are 4 balls and 4 urns. Each ball is placed in an urn, with the placement of each ball independent of the placement of the others. An urn is chosen at random; what is the probability that it will contain 2 balls? *Ans.* $54/256$.

14. The experiment in Prob. 13 is performed 4 times. What is the probability that an urn with 2 balls in it is chosen exactly once?

Ans. $4 \times 54/256 \times (202/256)^3$.

15. A number is chosen at random between 0 and 1. What is the probability that there is exactly one 7 in the first 10 decimal places? *Ans.* $9^9/10^9$.

16. A number is chosen at random between 0 and 1. What is the probability that exactly 5 of its first 10 decimal places are less than 5? *Ans.* $63/256$.

17. In a sequence of tosses of a coin a man stakes \$1 on heads at each toss. Let x be his net gain after n tosses. Find the probability function for x. *Ans.* $f(x) = {}^nC_{(n+x)/2}/2^n$.

18. A maze consists of equally spaced north-south paths and equally spaced east-west paths, intersecting to form a checkerboard array. A rat is started from some intersection and wanders through the maze in a completely aimless fashion, stopping at each intersection and choosing one of the 4 paths at random. Find the probability that the $2n$th intersection he comes to will be the one from which he started.

Ans. $({}^{2n}C_n)^2/16^n$.

19. Take a Bernoullian sequence of trials with $p = \frac{1}{3}$, and set up the probability function for the number of successes in 7 trials, 8 trials, 9 trials, 10 trials.

20. What is the most probable number of successes in each of the four cases in Prob. 19? *Ans.* 2, 2 or 3 (equally likely), 3, 3.

21. Show that the probability of r successes in n Bernoullian trials divided by the probability of $r + 1$ successes is $(r + 1)q/(n - r)p$.

22. Under what circumstances are there successive values of r that are equally likely? Hint: The ratio in Prob. 21 must equal unity.

Ans. When $(n + 1)p$ is an integer.

23. Show that the most probable value of r is the greatest integer less than or equal to $(n + 1)p$. Hint: The ratio in Prob. 21 increases as r increases. The most probable value of r is the first value for which this ratio is greater than unity.

24. When is 0 the most probable value of r? When is n the most probable value? *Ans.* When $p < 1/(n + 1)$; when $p > n/(n + 1)$.

25. Show that the probability of at least $r + 1$ successes in $n + 1$ Bernoullian trials is

$$(r + 1)\, {}^{n+1}C_{r+1} \int_0^p x^r(1 - x)^{n-r}\, dx.$$

Hint: See Prob. 26, Chap. 1.

26. Solve Prob. 7, Chap. 2, using Theorem III of this chapter.

27. What is the probability that at least one of the players in a bridge game will be dealt a complete suit of cards?

Ans. $[16 \times 13! \times 39! - 72 \times (13!)^2 \times 26! + 72 \times (13!)^4]/52!$.

28. What is the probability that the rat in Prob. 18 will return to his starting point at least once in the first 6 legs of his journey?

Ans. $1{,}345/4{,}096$.

29. An urn contains 5 white balls and 5 black balls. Ten times a ball is drawn and replaced. What is the probability that each of the white balls is drawn at least once?

Ans. $1 - 5(\frac{9}{10})^{10} + 10(\frac{8}{10})^{10} - 10(\frac{7}{10})^{10} + 5(\frac{6}{10})^{10} - (\frac{5}{10})^{10}$.

30. From a student body of 5,000, a student opinion poll takes a random sample of 200 student opinions. They do this by merely stopping a student on the campus, regardless of whether he has been questioned before or not. What is the probability that each of the 35 members of a certain fraternity will be questioned at least once?

$$Ans. \quad \sum_{r=0}^{35} (-1)^r \, {}^{35}C_r \left(\frac{5,000 - r}{5,000}\right)^{200}.$$

CHAPTER 5

MORE ABOUT STOCHASTIC VARIABLES

Throughout most of Chaps. 2 and 3 we have looked at the stochastic variable and its density function as the framework for the mathematical model of a physical situation. For all practical purposes what we have done is to jump from the physical situation to the stochastic variable and its density function and from there to the event space and the probabilities of events therein. However, this is for practical purposes only. A quick look at Definition 2, Chap. 2, will show that, while this point of view may be practical, it is fundamentally backward. The event space and its distribution function are the foundation elements of mathematical probability, and stochastic variables are functions defined over this space. The principal thesis of this chapter is just that. *A stochastic variable is a function.* The operations performed on stochastic variables in succeeding chapters will be much easier to understand if the student keeps this in mind.

34. Functions of Stochastic Variables

There is no reason why we should scrap the work we have done so far, however. Let us look at it this way: Certain stochastic variables (*viz.*, the coordinate variables) and their density functions serve to describe the event space. Thus, functions defined over the event space could be regarded as functions of these coordinate variables. That is, if a physical situation is represented by a variable x and its density function $f(x)$, then in general stochastic variables will be functions $u = u(x)$. In particular, $u(x) = x$ describes the coordinate variable itself as a function over the event space.

We are accustomed to seeing a density function (or probability function) associated with a stochastic variable; so the question might arise whether or not stochastic variables in general have such functions. The honest answer to this question is, "Not always." However, if, instead of describing probabilities as ordinary integrals of a density function, we described them as Stieltjes integrals of a distribution function (see Sec. 15), then the same form could be applied to all stochastic variables. In order to give as representative a picture as

76

we can of this important fact, let us discuss the special cases in which the forms we have adopted can be carried over.

The discrete case can be handled in general.

Theorem I.   Let S be an event space, discrete or continuous, with any number of dimensions.   Let u be a stochastic variable defined over S.   If the set of all possible values for u is a discrete set, then a probability function $g(u)$ is given by

$$g(a) = pr\{E_a\}$$

where E_a is the set of points in S for which $u = a$.

This is an immediate consequence of (d) of Theorem II, Chap. 2.

In the stochastic variable description of Bernoullian trials (Chap. 4) we have already seen an example of a discrete variable defined over a multidimensional space.   There u was the sum of the coordinate variables, and the sets E_a referred to in Theorem I were the sets of corner points on the "cube" contained in the hyperplanes $\Sigma x_i = a$.

It is worth noting that in Theorem I the only thing that has to be discrete is the set of values of u.   In a later section of this chapter we shall look at some discrete variables defined over continuous spaces.

Theorem II.   Let x be a stochastic variable with a density function $f(x)$, and let $u = u(x)$ be a strictly increasing (or strictly decreasing) function of x.   Then, u is a stochastic variable with a density function

$$g(u) = f[x(u)]|x'(u)|$$

where $x(u)$ is the inverse function to $u(x)$.

We want a function $g(u)$ such that

$$pr\{c \leq u \leq d\} = \int_c^d g(u)du$$

for every $c \leq d$.   Let $a = x(c)$ and $b = x(d)$.   Then, in the strictly increasing case, $c \leq u \leq d$ is equivalent to $a \leq x \leq b$, and

$$
\begin{aligned}
pr\{c \leq u \leq d\} &= pr\{a \leq x \leq b\} \\
&= \int_a^b f(x)dx \\
&= \int_c^d f[x(u)]x'(u)du
\end{aligned}
$$

by the familiar rules for change of variables in a definite integral. In this case $x'(u) \geq 0$ everywhere; so $|x'(u)| = x'(u)$, and the theorem is proved for the case of increasing u.

In the strictly decreasing case, $|x'(u)| = -x'(u)$, so that a minus sign is introduced. This is as it should be, however, because in this case $c \leq u \leq d$ is equivalent to $b \leq x \leq a$; so one set of limits of integration must be interchanged.

This is as near as we can come (on the first-year calculus level) to reducing the continuous case problem to a formula. However, Theorem II is too restricted to be of much use. The following informal suggestions will cover many important cases.

Theorem III (*Multidimensional Case*). If a stochastic variable u is defined over an event space of several dimensions, there are two suggested procedures for finding a density function for u:

(a) Find the set in the event space for which $t \leq u \leq t + dt$. Estimate the probability of this set from the joint density function, and apply (c) and (d) of Theorem V, Chap. 2, if possible.

(b) Find the set in the event space for which $u \leq t$. Integrate the joint density function over this set to find its probability, and apply (c') and (d') of Theorem V, Chap. 2, if possible.

Theorem IV (*Multivalued Case*). If a stochastic variable u fits Theorem II except that it is strictly increasing over some intervals of the x axis and strictly decreasing over others, apply Theorem II to each branch of the inverse function. Then, for each value of u, add the results to get $g(u)$.

Suppose x and y are stochastic variables and u is a function of x alone. Let us suppose u is strictly increasing; other cases follow at once by the application of Theorem IV. Then, the set for which $\alpha \leq u \leq \beta$ is the vertical strip in the xy plane defined by the inequalities $a \leq x \leq b$ where $\alpha = u(a)$ and $\beta = u(b)$. So, if x and y are independent, we have

$$pr\{\alpha \leq u \leq \beta \text{ and } c \leq y \leq d\} = pr\{a \leq x \leq b \text{ and } c \leq y \leq d\}$$
$$= pr\{a \leq x \leq b\}pr\{c \leq y \leq d\} = pr\{\alpha \leq u \leq \beta\}pr\{c \leq y \leq d\}.$$

That is [see (c) of Definition 2, Chap. 3], u and y are independent. Now, if v is a function of y alone, we apply the result just obtained to see that u and v are independent. Thus, we have proved the following:

Theorem V. If x and y are independent stochastic variables and if $u = u(x)$ and $v = v(y)$, then u and v are independent stochastic variables.

The examples in a later section of this chapter on normally distributed variables will serve to illustrate Theorem III. By way of illustration of Theorem IV, we might return to the problem of the time of disintegration of the radium atom (see Sec. 14).

In this problem we have a stochastic variable x with a density function

$$f(x) = \begin{cases} ke^{-kx} & \text{for } x \geq 0, \\ 0 & \text{for } x < 0. \end{cases}$$

In Chap. 6 we shall see that an important stochastic variable in connection with this problem is

$$u = \left(x - \frac{1}{k}\right)^2.$$

Now, the inverse function is

$$x = \pm \sqrt{u} + \frac{1}{k}$$

with the provision that $x \geq 0$. The picture:

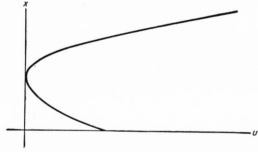

FIG. 13.

The inverse is double-valued for $0 \leq u \leq 1/k^2$ and single-valued for $u > 1/k^2$. Now

$$x'(u) = \pm \frac{1}{2\sqrt{u}};$$

hence on each branch of the double-valued section

$$|x'(u)| = \frac{1}{2\sqrt{u}}.$$

On the top branch

$$f[x(u)] = ke^{-k\sqrt{u}-1}.$$

On the bottom branch

$$f[x(u)] = ke^{k\sqrt{u}-1}.$$

Therefore,

$$g(u) = \begin{cases} 0 & \text{for } u < 0, \\[2ex] \dfrac{k}{2\sqrt{u}} \left(e^{k\sqrt{u}-1} + e^{-k\sqrt{u}-1}\right) = \dfrac{k}{e\sqrt{u}} \cosh(k\sqrt{u}) & \\[2ex] & \text{for } 0 \le u \le \dfrac{1}{k^2}, \\[2ex] \dfrac{k}{2\sqrt{u}} e^{-k\sqrt{u}-1} & \text{for } u > \dfrac{1}{k^2}. \end{cases}$$

35. Translation and Change of Scale

In many stochastic variable problems it is convenient to translate the axes—that is, if we have a stochastic variable x, to introduce a new stochastic variable $z = x - a$. Now, this new variable is merely a function of the old one; so if we have the density (or probability) function for x, we should be able to use Theorem II (or I) to get the density (or probability) function for z.

For the continuous case, $x(z) = z + a$; so $x'(z) = 1$. Thus, if $f(x)$ is the density function for x, the density function for z is $g(z) = f(z + a)$. The same result holds in the discrete case. $z = \alpha$ means $x = \alpha + a$; therefore, by Theorem I, $g(\alpha) = pr\{x = \alpha + a\} = f(\alpha + a)$. That is, $g(z) = f(z + a)$. Let us state this result formally.

Theorem VI. If x is a stochastic variable with a density (probability) function $f(x)$ and if $z = x - a$, then z is a stochastic variable with a density (probability) function $g(z) = f(z + a)$.

A transformation of the form $z = kx$ amounts to a change of scale on the x axis. This, too, is a useful operation on a stochastic variable, and we should do well to find out what it does to density and probability functions. Here, for the first time, we see the essential difference between density functions and probability functions. We have emphasized the analogy between the continuous and discrete cases until the student may wonder why density and probability functions even have different names. The crucial point is that the density function is multiplied by dx before being added (integrated), while the probability function is not. This distinction shows up very clearly in the two *different* formulas for the new function after a change of scale.

Theorem VII (*Discrete Case*). If x is a stochastic variable with a probability function $f(x)$ and if $z = kx$, then z is a stochastic variable with a probability function $g(z) = f(z/k)$.

This follows immediately from Theorem I. $z = \alpha$ means $x = \alpha/k$, and Theorem I gives us the desired result.

Theorem VIII (*Continuous Case*). If x is a stochastic variable with a density function $f(x)$ and if $z = kx$, then z is a stochastic variable with a density function $g(z) = (1/k)f(z/k)$.

The inverse function $x(z) = z/k$; so $x'(z) = 1/k$, and this result follows from Theorem II.

36. Representation of Physical Situations

This section consists of a brief digression in the form of some examples of a procedure which is not very practical but which might help to illustrate and emphasize the fact that fundamentally a stochastic variable is a function. The method of Chaps. 2 and 3 is by far the most common in the representation of physical situations. There we let the values of the coordinate variable (or variables) represent the physical events in a natural way and then chose a density function (or probability function) that would properly describe the probabilities. Now, suppose we go at it from the point of view of the axioms and the definition of a stochastic variable (Definition 2, Chap. 2). That is, let us just pull out of thin air an event space with a distribution function satisfying the axioms. This space may seem to have no particular connection with any physical situation, but let us try to construct stochastic variables (*i.e.*, functions) over it that will represent the events in a physical situation.

For the remainder of this section, let the event space be the unit interval $0 \leq x \leq 1$ with the probability of each subinterval defined as its length. That is, let the coordinate variable x have a density function identically 1 in the interval, zero outside.

Over this event space let us find stochastic variables which describe the physical situations in the illustrative examples of Chap. 2. In the discrete case the best way to do this is by inspection, keeping Theorem I in mind.

If $u(x)$ is the total thrown on two dice, we have:

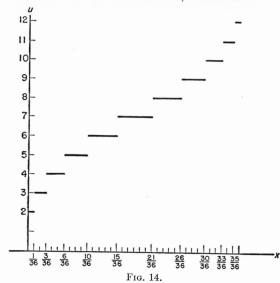

Fig. 14.

For the balls drawn from the urn, we have:

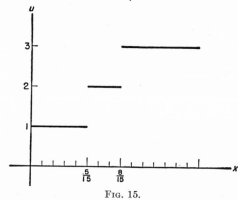

Fig. 15.

To get the continuous cases, we note that according to Theorem II, since $f(x) = 1$, we have

$$g(u) = |x'(u)|.$$

Now, if we fix it so the signs are right, we shall have

$$g(u) = x'(u).$$

That is, the density function for u is the derivative of the inverse function to u. So, if we look in Chap. 2 and find out what density functions we want, to get the function u we integrate and then take the inverse.

In the problem on the bombardment of a hemispherical screen, we want

$$g(u) = \cos u;$$

therefore

$$x(u) = \int_0^u \cos t \, dt = \sin u,$$

and

$$u(x) = \arcsin x.$$

The picture:

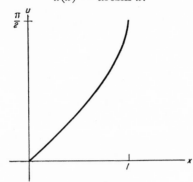

FIG. 16.

In the radium atom problem, we want

$$g(u) = ke^{-ku};$$

therefore

$$x(u) = \int_0^u ke^{-kt} \, dt = 1 - e^{-ku},$$

and

$$u(x) = -\frac{1}{k} \log(1 - x).$$

The picture:

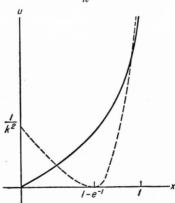

FIG. 17.

Earlier in this chapter we mentioned the variable $[u - (1/k)]^2$ in connection with this problem. From the above representation for u, we find this very quickly:

$$v(x) = \left(u - \frac{1}{k}\right)^2 = \frac{1}{k^2}[\log(1 - x) + 1]^2.$$

This function is shown by the dotted line in Fig. 17.

On applying Theorem IV to the stochastic variable $v(x)$, we get

$$x(v) = 1 - e^{\pm k\sqrt{v}-1};$$

$$|x'(v)| = \frac{k}{2\sqrt{v}}\,e^{\pm k\sqrt{v}-1}.$$

The minus sign in the exponent applies to the branch that goes all the way out. The plus sign applies to the branch that goes only to $1/k^2$. Since $f[x(v)] = 1$, we get $g(v)$ by merely taking the proper values of $|x'(v)|$. From 0 to $1/k^2$ we must add the two exponentials to get a hyperbolic cosine. From $1/k^2$ to ∞ we have only the negative exponential. This gives us the same result we had before:

$$g(v) = \begin{cases} 0 & \text{for } v < 0, \\ \dfrac{k}{e\sqrt{v}}\cosh(k\sqrt{v}) & \text{for } 0 \le v \le \dfrac{1}{k^2}, \\ \dfrac{k}{2\sqrt{v}}\,e^{-k\sqrt{v}-1} & \text{for } v > \dfrac{1}{k^2}. \end{cases}$$

37. Sums and Products

The general subject of functions of stochastic variables is one that could well occupy an entire book. The individual values observed in a sampling process are stochastic variables, and the statistician is interested in all kinds of functions of these variables. We shall not attempt to give a representative discussion of sampling distributions here. Suffice it to say that a great number of problems in mathematical statistics are concerned with specific examples of the operations suggested in Theorems I to IV.

In probability theory proper, however, we frequently want to deal with the sum and the product of two (or more) stochastic variables. Any such combination of functions over an event space is, of course, just another function over the event space.

We have already seen several sums of stochastic variables. In the example of the two dice (as treated in Chap. 3) we found the sum of the two variables to be significant.   In the stochastic variable representation of Bernoullian trials we used the sum of n variables.

We have not looked at any products yet, but the principle is the same.   Only the details are different.   In the problem of two dice, the event space is a square array of 36 points.   Now, we let $u = xy$, and (see Theorem I) pick out the sets E_a for which $u = a$:

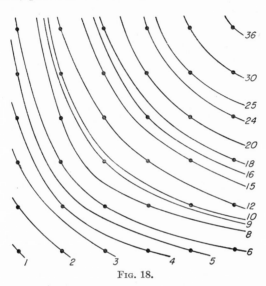

Fig. 18.

So we have the probability function

u:	1	2	3	4	5	6	8	9	10
$g(u)$:	$\frac{1}{36}$	$\frac{2}{36}$	$\frac{2}{36}$	$\frac{3}{36}$	$\frac{2}{36}$	$\frac{4}{36}$	$\frac{2}{36}$	$\frac{1}{36}$	$\frac{2}{36}$
u:	12	15	16	18	20	24	25	30	36
$g(u)$:	$\frac{4}{36}$	$\frac{2}{36}$	$\frac{1}{36}$	$\frac{2}{36}$	$\frac{2}{36}$	$\frac{2}{36}$	$\frac{1}{36}$	$\frac{2}{36}$	$\frac{1}{36}$

By means of Theorem II or III we could (if we could integrate everything) find the density function for the product of two continuous variables.   Fortunately, most of the work in the theory of probability can be carried on without finding these density functions.   It will appear later (see Chap. 6) that the moments of a stochastic variable give us most of the information we want, and these moments can frequently be found for sums and products without getting the density functions for the sums and products themselves.   The point we want to make here is that the sums and products of stochastic variables are just other stochastic variables and have their density functions or probability functions whether it is convenient to find them or not.   So, when we speak (as in Chap. 8) of

$$pr \left\{ a \leq \sum_{i=1}^{n} x_i \leq b \right\}$$

we are just talking about the probability of a pair of inequalities on a stochastic variable, no matter what means we use to evaluate such probabilities.

There is one mistaken picture of sums and products that the student should be warned against. We have seen earlier in this chapter that, if we take the unit interval with a constant density function as the event space, we can describe a large variety of physical situations by means of functions over this space. Now, why not take two functions over the unit interval, multiply (or add) them together point by point, and call the result the product (or sum) of the two? In the case of the two dice, this would give the product the values 1, 4, 9, 16, 25, 36, with probabilities $\frac{1}{6}$ each—something completely different from what we got above. The fallacy in this interpretation of sum and product is that it overlooks the fundamental idea of Chap. 3 that two or more stochastic variables are used to describe compound events and that a *joint* density function is called for to give probabilities for *all* these compound events. When we put the two stochastic variables (functions) over the same *one-dimensional* space, we do not represent all the compound events at all. The representation of $x + y$ and xy as the sum and product, respectively, of two functions over an event space is *not* this

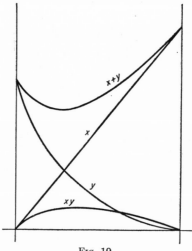

Fig. 19.

but this

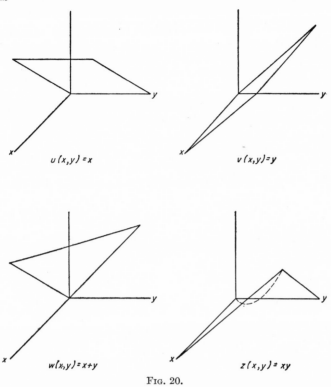

$u\,(x,y)=x$ $v\,(x,y)=y$

$w(x,y)=x+y$ $z\,(x,y)=xy$

FIG. 20.

If, in the above picture of the variable xy, we impose the restriction $y = x$, we get the parabola indicated by the dotted line. Thus, if the variables are necessarily equal, the product xy reduces to x^2; and the three-dimensional picture may be replaced by a two-dimensional one. The student should note the distinction between *identical* stochastic variables and *equal* stochastic variables. Two stochastic variables are identical if their marginal distributions are the same, but this involves no particular dependence of one on the other. Indeed, in many applications we have use for identical variables which are completely independent. Equal variables, on the other hand, have all points of their joint distribution on the line $y = x$.

As a case in point, let us consider variables x and y, each of which represents the result of throwing a single die. Here each of the variables x^2 and y^2 is the product of equal variables and so assumes the values 1, 4, 9, 16, 25, 36, with probability $\frac{1}{6}$ each. The variable xy, on the other hand, is the product of identical but independent variables and has the probability function given at the start of this section.

38. Convolutions

Let x and y be independent stochastic variables with density functions $f(x)$ and $g(y)$, respectively. Then

$$\varphi(x,y) = f(x)g(y)$$

is their joint density function. Let $F(x)$ be the distribution function for x; that is,

$$pr\{x \le t\} = F(t).$$

Then, by (d) of Theorem IV, Chap. 2,

$$F'(x) = f(x).$$

Now, we want to find the density function for the variable $x + y$. First, we note that the set of points for which $x + y \le u$ is the lower left half plane (shaded in the diagram).

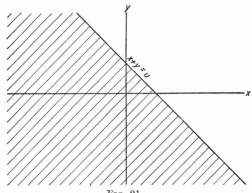

Fig. 21.

Therefore, the distribution function

$$H(u) = pr\{x + y \le u\}$$

is the integral of $\varphi(x,y)$ over this shaded area:

$$H(u) = \int_{-\infty}^{\infty} \int_{-\infty}^{u-y} f(x)g(y)dx\,dy$$
$$= \int_{-\infty}^{\infty} F(u - y)g(y)dy.$$

The required density function $h(u)$ is the derivative of H; so we differentiate the above equation with respect to u. This calls for differentiation under the integral sign—a step that requires justification. However, we shall skip that part of the proof and proceed to differentiate. This gives us

$$h(u) = \int_{-\infty}^{\infty} f(u - y)g(y)dy.$$

Clearly, we could have integrated in the other order and obtained

$$h(u) = \int_{-\infty}^{\infty} g(u - x)f(x)dx.$$

The two (necessarily equal) integrals obtained here define what is called the *convolution* of f and g. Frequently this result is written symbolically

$$h = f * g.$$

These results may be summed up as follows:

Theorem IX. If x and y are independent stochastic variables with density functions f and g, respectively, then the stochastic variable $u = x + y$ has the density function

$$h(u) = f(u) * g(u) = \int_{-\infty}^{\infty} f(u - y)g(y)dy = \int_{-\infty}^{\infty} g(u - x)f(x)dx.$$

For example, suppose x and y are chosen independently and at random between 0 and 1. Then,

$$f(x) = \begin{cases} 1 & \text{for } 0 \le x \le 1, \\ 0 & \text{otherwise,} \end{cases}$$

$$g(y) = \begin{cases} 1 & \text{for } 0 \le y \le 1, \\ 0 & \text{otherwise.} \end{cases}$$

Therefore,

$$f(u - y) = \begin{cases} 1 & \text{for } u - 1 \le y \le u, \\ 0 & \text{otherwise.} \end{cases}$$

So, for $0 \le u \le 1$,

$$f(u - y)g(y) = \begin{cases} 1 & \text{for } 0 \le y \le u, \\ 0 & \text{otherwise;} \end{cases}$$

if $1 < u \le 2$,

$$f(u - y)g(y) = \begin{cases} 1 & \text{for } u - 1 \le y \le 1, \\ 0 & \text{otherwise.} \end{cases}$$

For all other values of u, $f(u - y)g(y)$ is identically zero. Therefore,

$$f(u) * g(u) = \begin{cases} \int_0^u 1 \, dy = u & \text{for } 0 \le u \le 1, \\ \int_{u-1}^1 1 \, dy = 2 - u & \text{for } 1 < u \le 2, \\ 0 & \text{otherwise.} \end{cases}$$

The picture:

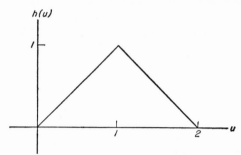

FIG. 22.

For certain discrete cases we get something that looks like a convolution directly from Theorem I. According to that theorem, $h(u)$ is the sum of all values of $f(x)g(y)$ for which $x + y = u$. Clearly, we can organize such a summation by setting $x = u - y$ and summing on y; that is,

$$h(u) = \sum_y f(u - y)g(y),$$

the summation taken over all pertinent values of y.

For example, suppose

$$f(x) = {}^nC_x p^x q^{n-x} \quad (x = 0, 1, 2, \ldots, n),$$
$$g(y) = {}^nC_y p^y q^{n-y} \quad (y = 0, 1, 2, \ldots, n).$$

Of course, this means that x and y are each the number of successes in n Bernoullian trials; so, obviously, $x + y$ is the number of successes in $2n$ trials, and

$$h(u) = {}^{2n}C_u p^u q^{2n-u} \quad (u = 0, 1, 2, \ldots, 2n).$$

However, let us verify this by the methods of this chapter. Here

$$h(u) = \sum_y f(u - y)g(y)$$

$$= \sum_y {}^nC_{u-y} p^{u-y} q^{n-u+y} \; {}^nC_y p^y q^{n-y}$$

$$= \sum_y {}^nC_y \, {}^nC_{u-y} p^u q^{2n-u}$$

$$= p^u q^{2n-u} \sum_y {}^nC_y \, {}^nC_{u-y}.$$

For $u \leq n$, the summation is from 0 to u; and Prob. 23, Chap. 1, gives the result immediately. For $u > n$, the summation is from $u - n$ to n; and the substitutions $z = n - y$ and $v = 2n - u$ reduce this to the previous case.

39. Normal Distributions

The so-called normal, or Gaussian, distribution is the one determined by a density function of the form

$$g(z) = \frac{1}{\sigma \sqrt{2\pi}} e^{-(z-a)^2/2\sigma^2}.$$

If we make the translation $x = z - a$, we find from Theorem VI that the density function for x is

$$f(x) = g(x + a) = \frac{1}{\sigma \sqrt{2\pi}} e^{-x^2/2\sigma^2}.$$

Though the first form given above is usually regarded as the general definition of the normal distribution, we shall always assume that the translation has been made. Thus, when we speak of a normal distribution, we shall mean the simpler form in which $a = 0$. The significance of the constant σ we shall see in Chap. 6. The importance of this density function in probability theory will appear in Chap. 8. For the present, we want to study an important special property of normally distributed stochastic variables that illustrates some of the ideas in this chapter.

Before doing that, however, we should show that what we have called a density function for the normal distribution really is one, $i.\ e.$, that

$$\int_{-\infty}^{\infty} f(x)dx = 1.$$

The indefinite integral

$$\Phi(t) = \int_{-\infty}^{t} \frac{1}{\sigma \sqrt{2\pi}} e^{-x^2/2\sigma^2} \, dx$$

is a "new" function, not expressible in terms of elementary operations. Like trigonometric functions and logarithms, its values have been tabulated extensively, but this does not do us much good at the moment. The following trick is ordinarily used to evaluate the integral over the entire x axis:

$$\left(\int_{-\infty}^{\infty} \frac{1}{\sigma \sqrt{2\pi}} e^{-x^2/2\sigma^2} \, dx \right)^2 = \frac{1}{2\pi\sigma^2} \int_{-\infty}^{\infty} e^{-x^2/2\sigma^2} \, dx \int_{-\infty}^{\infty} e^{-y^2/2\sigma^2} \, dy$$

$$= \frac{1}{2\pi\sigma^2} \int_{-\infty}^{\infty} \int_{-\infty}^{\infty} e^{-(x^2+y^2)/2\sigma^2} \, dx \, dy$$

Now, we change to polar coordinates and remember that the element of area $dx\, dy$ becomes $r\, dr\, d\theta$.

$$\left(\int_{-\infty}^{\infty} \frac{1}{\sigma\sqrt{2\pi}}\, e^{-x^2/2\sigma^2}\, dx\right)^2 = \frac{1}{2\pi}\int_0^{2\pi}\int_0^{\infty} e^{-r^2/2\sigma^2}\, \frac{r}{\sigma^2}\, dr\, d\theta$$

$$= \frac{1}{2\pi}\int_0^{2\pi} \left.- e^{-r^2/2\sigma^2}\right|_0^{\infty} d\theta = \frac{1}{2\pi}\int_0^{2\pi} d\theta = 1.$$

Theorem X. Any linear combination of two independent normally distributed stochastic variables is itself a normally distributed stochastic variable.

Let x and y be independent stochastic variables with density functions

$$\frac{1}{\sigma_1\sqrt{2\pi}}\, e^{-x^2/2\sigma_1^2} \qquad \text{and} \qquad \frac{1}{\sigma_2\sqrt{2\pi}}\, e^{-y^2/2\sigma_2^2},$$

respectively, and let $u = ax + by$. Now, let $z = ax$ and $w = by$; then by Theorem VIII the density functions for z and w are

$$\frac{1}{\alpha\sqrt{2\pi}}\, e^{-z^2/2\alpha^2} \qquad \text{and} \qquad \frac{1}{\beta\sqrt{2\pi}}\, e^{-w^2/2\beta^2},$$

respectively, where $\alpha = a\sigma_1$ and $\beta = b\sigma_2$. By Theorem V, z and w are independent, and $u = z + w$; so Theorem IX applies, and

$$h(u) = \int_{-\infty}^{\infty} \frac{1}{2\pi\alpha\beta}\, e^{-(u-w)^2/2\alpha^2} e^{-w^2/2\beta^2}\, dw$$

$$= \int_{-\infty}^{\infty} \frac{1}{2\pi\alpha\beta}\, \exp\left(-\frac{\beta^2 u^2 - 2\beta^2 uw + \beta^2 w^2 + \alpha^2 w^2}{2\alpha^2\beta^2}\right) dw.$$

On completing the square in the exponent, we have

$$h(u) = \frac{1}{2\pi\alpha\beta}\int_{-\infty}^{\infty} \exp\left[-\frac{\alpha^2 + \beta^2}{2\alpha^2\beta^2}\left(w - \frac{\beta^2 u}{\alpha^2 + \beta^2}\right)^2 - \frac{u^2}{2(\alpha^2 + \beta^2)}\right] dw$$

$$= \frac{1}{\sqrt{2\pi(\alpha^2 + \beta^2)}}\, \exp\left[-\frac{u^2}{2(\alpha^2 + \beta^2)}\right] \int_{-\infty}^{\infty} \frac{\sqrt{\alpha^2 + \beta^2}}{\alpha\beta\sqrt{2\pi}}$$

$$\exp\left[-\frac{\alpha^2 + \beta^2}{2\alpha^2\beta^2}\left(w - \frac{\beta^2 u}{\alpha^2 + \beta^2}\right)^2\right] dw,$$

and this last integral is equal to 1; therefore the density function for u is

$$h(u) = \frac{1}{\sqrt{2\pi(\alpha^2 + \beta^2)}}\, e^{-u^2/2(\alpha^2+\beta^2)}.$$

Thus, u is a normally distributed stochastic variable with

$$\sigma = \sqrt{\alpha^2 + \beta^2} = \sqrt{a^2\sigma_1^2 + b^2\sigma_2^2}.$$

By applying this theorem over and over again, we obtain the following result:

Corollary 1.   If x_1, x_2, . . . , x_n are independent stochastic variables with density functions

$$f_i(x_i) = \frac{1}{\sigma_i \sqrt{2\pi}} \, e^{-x_i^2/2\sigma_i^2},$$

then

$$u = \sum_{i=1}^n a_i x_i$$

is a stochastic variable with a density function

$$h(u) = \frac{1}{\sqrt{2\pi(\alpha_1^2 + \alpha_2^2 + \cdots + \alpha_n^2)}} \exp\left[-\frac{u^2}{2(\alpha_1^2 + \alpha_2^2 + \cdots + \alpha_n^2)}\right]$$

where $\alpha_i = a_i\sigma_i$.

In the case of the so-called circular normal distribution in the plane, the joint density function is

$$\varphi(x,y) = \frac{1}{2\pi\sigma^2} \, e^{-(x^2+y^2)/2\sigma^2}$$

$$= \frac{1}{2\pi\sigma^2} \, e^{-r^2/2\sigma^2}$$

where $r = \sqrt{x^2 + y^2}$.   Now, the fact that the *joint* density function is a function of r alone does not make it the density function for r.   As a matter of fact, surprising as it may seem, in this case r is not normally distributed.   Let us apply (a) of Theorem III.   Note that the inequalities $t \le r \le t + dt$ define a ring, and it is this ring whose probability we want.   The probability of this ring is approximately

$$\frac{1}{2\pi\sigma^2} \, e^{-t^2/2\sigma^2} A$$

where A is the area of the ring.   Now, A is approximately $2\pi t \, dt$; so

$$pr\{t \le r \le t + dt\} \simeq \frac{t}{\sigma^2} \, e^{-t^2/2\sigma^2} \, dt,$$

and (d) of Theorem V, Chap. II, tells us that r has the density function

$$f(r) = \frac{r}{\sigma^2} e^{-r^2/2\sigma^2}.$$

REFERENCES FOR FURTHER STUDY

Halmos, "The Foundations of Probability," *Am. Math. Monthly,* vol. 51, pp. 493–510, 1944.

Kolmogoroff, *Foundations of the Theory of Probability.*

Uspensky, *Introduction to Mathematical Probability,* Chaps. XIII, XVI.

PROBLEMS

1. Let x have a density function identically 1 from 0 to 1. Describe the stochastic variable of Prob. 30, Chap. 2, as a function of x.
Ans. $u(x) = \sin \pi(x - \tfrac{1}{2})$.

2. Let x be as in Prob. 1. Describe a variable with Cauchy's distribution (Prob. 31, Chap. 2) as a function of x.
Ans. $u(x) = \tan \pi(x - \tfrac{1}{2})$.

3. Find the probability function for the sum of the variables in Prob. 30, Chap. 3.
Ans.

u:	2	3	4	5	6
$h(u)$:	$\tfrac{1}{12}$	$\tfrac{7}{36}$	$\tfrac{35}{72}$	$\tfrac{1}{6}$	$\tfrac{5}{72}$

4. Find the probability function for the product of these variables:
Ans.

u:	1	2	3	4	6	9
$h(u)$:	$\tfrac{1}{12}$	$\tfrac{7}{36}$	$\tfrac{31}{72}$	$\tfrac{1}{18}$	$\tfrac{1}{6}$	$\tfrac{5}{72}$

5. Find the probability function for the sum of the variables in Prob. 31, Chap. 3.
Ans.

u:	2	3	4	5	6
$h(u)$:	$\tfrac{1}{10}$	$\tfrac{1}{5}$	$\tfrac{2}{5}$	$\tfrac{1}{5}$	$\tfrac{1}{10}$

6. Find the probability function for the product of these variables:
Ans.

u:	1	2	3	4	6	9
$h(u)$:	$\tfrac{1}{10}$	$\tfrac{1}{5}$	$\tfrac{1}{5}$	$\tfrac{1}{5}$	$\tfrac{1}{5}$	$\tfrac{1}{10}$

7. Find the probability function for the sum of the squares of these variables:
Ans.

u:	2	5	8	10	13	18
$h(u)$:	$\tfrac{1}{10}$	$\tfrac{1}{5}$	$\tfrac{1}{5}$	$\tfrac{1}{5}$	$\tfrac{1}{5}$	$\tfrac{1}{10}$

8. Let $\varphi(x,y) = x + y$ in the unit square $0 \le x \le 1$, $0 \le y \le 1$ with $\varphi = 0$ elsewhere. Find the density function for $x + y$.

Ans.
$$h(u) = \begin{cases} u^2 & \text{for } 0 \le u \le 1, \\ 2u - u^2 & \text{for } 1 < u \le 2, \\ 0 & \text{otherwise.} \end{cases}$$

9. Using the joint density function in Prob. 8, find the density function for xy.
Ans. $h(u) = 2 - 2u$ for $0 \le u \le 1$, $h = 0$ otherwise.

10. Let x and y be chosen independently and at random between 0 and 1. Find the density function for xy.

      Ans. $h(u) = \log(1/u)$ for $0 < u \leq 1$, $h = 0$ otherwise.

11. Let x and y be as in Prob. 10. Let $u = \max. (x,y)$. Find the density function for u.

      Ans. $h(u) = 2u$ for $0 \leq u \leq 1$, $h = 0$ otherwise.

12. For the same x and y, find the density function for $v = \min.(x,y)$.

      Ans. $k(v) = 2 - 2v$ for $0 \leq v \leq 1$, $k = 0$ otherwise.

13. Find the joint density function for the variables u and v of Probs. 11 and 12. Note that x and y are independent, but u and v are not.

      Ans. $\varphi(u,v) = 2$ for $0 \leq v \leq u$, $0 \leq u \leq 1$, $\varphi = 0$ otherwise.

14. Let x and y be independent and have density functions

$$f(x) = \begin{cases} \alpha e^{-\alpha x} & \text{for } x \geq 0, \\ 0 & \text{for } x < 0, \end{cases} \qquad g(y) = \begin{cases} \beta e^{-\beta y} & \text{for } y \geq 0, \\ 0 & \text{for } y < 0, \end{cases}$$

respectively. Find the density function for $x + y$.

      Ans. $h(u) = \dfrac{\alpha\beta}{\beta - \alpha} (e^{-\alpha u} - e^{-\beta u})$ for $u \geq 0$, $h = 0$ for $u < 0$.

15. If $\alpha = \beta$, the answer to Prob. 14 is meaningless. Find the density function for u in this case.

      Ans. $h(u) = \alpha^2 u e^{-\alpha u}$ for $u \geq 0$, $h = 0$ for $u < 0$.

16. Let x and y be independent, and let each of them have Cauchy's distribution (Prob. 31, Chap. 2). Find the density function for $x + y$.

      Ans. $h(u) = 2/\pi(4 + u^2)$.

17. Let x and y be independent, and let each of them have Poisson's distribution (Prob. 23, Chap. 2). Find the probability function for $x + y$. Hint: See Prob. 21, Chap. 1.   *Ans.* $h(u) = (2a)^u e^{-2a}/u!$.

18. Let x be chosen at random between -1 and 1. Find the density function for x^2.

      Ans. $h(u) = 1/2 \sqrt{u}$ for $0 < u \leq 1$, $h = 0$ otherwise.

19. Let x have the density function $f(x) = e^{-x}$ for $x \geq 0$ with $f = 0$ for $x < 0$. Find the density function for x^2.

      Ans. $h(u) = (1/2 \sqrt{u})e^{-\sqrt{u}}$ for $u > 0$, $h = 0$ otherwise.

20. Compute the first two derivatives of the density function $(1/\sigma \sqrt{2\pi})e^{-x^2/2\sigma^2}$. Find its maxima, minima, and inflection points, and draw a graph.   *Ans.* Max. at 0, no min., infl. pts. at $\pm\sigma$.

21. Let x be a normally distributed variable with $\sigma = 1$. Find the density function for x^2.

      Ans. $h(u) = (1/\sqrt{2\pi u})e^{-u/2}$ for $u > 0$, $h = 0$ otherwise.

22. Let x and y be independent, and let each of them be normally distributed with $\sigma = 1$. Find the density function for $x^2 + y^2$.

Hint: The density function for $\sqrt{x^2 + y^2}$ is found in the text (Sec. 39).   Ans. $h(u) = \frac{1}{2}e^{-u/2}$ for $u \geq 0$, $h = 0$ otherwise.

23. Show from Probs. 21 and 22 that

$$\int_0^u \frac{dx}{\sqrt{x(u - x)}} = \pi.$$

Hint: Compare the convolution for Prob. 22 with the answer obtained by other methods.

24. If x is normally distributed, find the density function for e^x.

Ans. $h(u) = \dfrac{1}{\sigma u \sqrt{2\pi}} e^{-(\log u)^2/2\sigma^2}$ for $u > 0$, $h = 0$ otherwise.

25. The magnitude of a certain physical characteristic (such as height, weight, and velocity) is normally distributed over the members of a certain large population.   An experimenter chooses members of this population at random and measures this characteristic for each member chosen.   His measuring process is susceptible to error, and the probability distribution for the errors is also normal and independent of the magnitude he is measuring.   Show that there is a normal probability distribution for the result of a given measurement. Hint: Apply Theorem X.

26. Show that, if there is a normal probability distribution for the results (note that this is not quite the same as to say that the aggregate of results form a normal frequency distribution) and if the law of error is normal and independent of the magnitude being measured, then there is a normal probability distribution for the true measurement of an item chosen at random from the population.

27. Show that if $x_1, x_2, \ldots, x_n$ are the values of n independent samples drawn from a normally distributed population, then the sample mean

$$u = \frac{1}{n} \sum_{i=1}^{n} x_i$$

is a normally distributed variable.

CHAPTER 6

MOMENTS

No study of stochastic variables would be complete without a discussion of moments. Not only are the moments of a stochastic variable invaluable tools for the statistician, but some knowledge of them is necessary for an understanding of the limit theorems (see Chap. 8), which are the core of the calculus of probabilities itself.

The student has probably first heard of the term "moment" in connection with the law of levers in elementary physics. Most first-year calculus courses attempt some further discussion of the idea, but still the terminology of physics (centroid, moment of inertia, etc.) is ordinarily used. The student may therefore get the idea that a moment is something fundamentally connected with rotating rigid bodies.

To the mathematician moment merely means a Stieltjes integral of a certain type. So in our discussion it means either integral or sum as the case may be—see Sec. 15. The moments of the physicist are examples of this type of integral. So are those of the statistician, and it is these latter that we shall be interested in here.

40. Moments of a Stochastic Variable

Without Stieltjes integrals, we need separate definitions of moments for the discrete and continuous cases.

Definition 1. The kth moment of the stochastic variable x about the point a is defined as follows:

(*a*) *Discrete Case*

$$\sum_{x \text{ in } S} (x - a)^k f(x),$$

(*b*) *Continuous Case*

$$\int_{-\infty}^{\infty} (x - a)^k f(x)dx.$$

If (*a*) involves an infinite series or if (*b*) involves an improper integral, this series or integral must be absolutely convergent. Otherwise, we say the moment is not defined.

This condition of absolute convergence is not, of course, automatically satisfied. Our chief concern will be with the formal manipulation of certain moments; so we shall make the blanket hypothesis that, unless otherwise noted, all moments mentioned in subsequent theorems are assumed to be defined. As we pointed out in Chap. 3, the order of integration may be changed in an absolutely convergent multiple integral; so we shall continue to do this as a matter of course.

To certain moments of stochastic variables the statistician gives special names and attaches special symbols. The first moment about zero is called the *mean*, or *expectation*, and is denoted by $\bar{x}$ or $E(x)$—whichever symbol seems more convenient. In symbols:

$$E(x) = \bar{x} = \int_{-\infty}^{\infty} x f(x)dx.$$

The second moment about the mean is called the *variance*, or *dispersion*. (We shall use the former term exclusively.) It is denoted by var(x) or, frequently, by σ^2. In symbols:

$$\text{var}(x) = \sigma^2 = \int_{-\infty}^{\infty} (x - \bar{x})^2 f(x)dx.$$

The positive square root of the variance is called the *standard deviation*. As one might suspect, it is denoted by σ.

41. Example—Normal Distributions

First, we might take a look at the moments of a normally distributed variable. Accordingly, let

$$f(x) = \frac{1}{\sigma \sqrt{2\pi}} e^{-x^2/2\sigma^2}.$$

Now,

$$E(x) = \frac{1}{\sigma \sqrt{2\pi}} \int_{-\infty}^{\infty} xe^{-x^2/2\sigma^2}\,dx = -\frac{\sigma}{\sqrt{2\pi}} e^{-x^2/2\sigma^2}\bigg|_{-\infty}^{\infty} = 0.$$

So the interesting moments are those about zero. Let us denote by M_n the nth moment about zero. To find M_n in general, we take

$$x^n e^{-x^2/2\sigma^2}\,dx$$

and factor it as

$$(x^{n-1})(xe^{-x^2/2\sigma^2}\,dx).$$

Then, integrating by parts, we have the recursion formula:

$$M_n = \frac{1}{\sigma\sqrt{2\pi}} \int_{-\infty}^{\infty} x^n e^{-x^2/2\sigma^2}\, dx$$

$$= -\frac{\sigma}{\sqrt{2\pi}} x^{n-1} e^{-x^2/2\sigma^2} \Big|_{-\infty}^{\infty} + \frac{\sigma(n-1)}{\sqrt{2\pi}} \int_{-\infty}^{\infty} x^{n-2} e^{-x^2/2\sigma^2}\, dx$$

$$= \frac{\sigma(n-1)}{\sqrt{2\pi}} \int_{-\infty}^{\infty} x^{n-2} e^{-x^2/2\sigma^2}\, dx$$

$$= \sigma^2(n-1)M_{n-2}.$$

We know from Sec. 39 that $M_0 = 1$, and we have just seen that $M_1 = 0$. Therefore, it follows that all the odd moments are zero, while the even moments run σ^2, $3\sigma^4$, $15\sigma^6$, $\ldots$ with the moment of order $2n$ given by $1 \times 3 \times 5 \times 7 \cdots (2n-1)\sigma^{2n}$.

In particular, we see that $\mathrm{var}(x) = \sigma^2$; so the constant σ, which appeared merely as a parameter in our discussion of normal distributions in Sec. 39, is actually the standard deviation of the variable x.

42. Example—Cauchy's Distribution

It would be fallacious to argue in the above example that the odd moments are zero because the density function is symmetric with respect to 0. It is true that for an odd moment this gives a first quadrant "area" and a congruent third quadrant "area." Therefore, if the moment exists, it must be zero; but a doubly improper integral is not absolutely convergent unless it is finite at each end. If both the areas mentioned above are infinite, we say the moment does not exist.

As an example of this sort of thing, consider the stochastic variable x with density function

$$f(x) = \frac{1}{\pi(1+x^2)}.$$

This is usually referred to as Cauchy's distribution (see Prob. 31, Chap. 2). Note that

$$\int_{-\infty}^{\infty} \frac{1}{\pi(1+x^2)}\, dx = \frac{1}{\pi} \arctan x \Big|_{-\infty}^{\infty} = \frac{1}{\pi}\left[\frac{\pi}{2} - \left(-\frac{\pi}{2}\right)\right] = 1,$$

as required. However,

$$\int_{-\infty}^{\infty} \frac{x}{\pi(1+x^2)}\, dx = \frac{1}{\pi} \log(1+x^2) \Big|_{-\infty}^{\infty},$$

and this integral tends to infinity on each end. So we say the first moment of this stochastic variable is not defined.

43. Example—The Radium Atom

We have seen (Sec. 14) that, if x is the time of disintegration of a given atom of radium, then x is a stochastic variable with

$$f(x) = \begin{cases} ke^{-kx} & \text{for } x \geq 0, \\ 0 & \text{for } x < 0. \end{cases}$$

So in this case we have

$$\begin{aligned} E(x) &= \int_0^\infty kxe^{-kx}\, dx \\ &= -xe^{-kx}\Big|_0^\infty + \int_0^\infty e^{-kx}\, dx \\ &= -\frac{1}{k}\, e^{-kx}\Big|_0^\infty \\ &= \frac{1}{k}. \end{aligned}$$

Our interest (in Chap. 5) in the variable $[x - (1/k)]^2$ stems from the fact that

$$\begin{aligned} \operatorname{var}(x) &= \int_0^\infty k\left(x - \frac{1}{k}\right)^2 e^{-kx}\, dx \\ &= -\left(x - \frac{1}{k}\right)^2 e^{-kx}\Big|_0^\infty + \int_0^\infty 2\left(x - \frac{1}{k}\right) e^{-kx}\, dx \\ &= \frac{1}{k^2} - \left[\frac{2}{k}\left(x - \frac{1}{k}\right) e^{-kx}\right]_0^\infty + \int_0^\infty \frac{2}{k} e^{-kx}\, dx \\ &= \frac{1}{k^2} - \frac{2}{k^2} - \left[\frac{2}{k^2} e^{-kx}\right]_0^\infty \\ &= \frac{1}{k^2} - \frac{2}{k^2} + \frac{2}{k^2} \\ &= \frac{1}{k^2}. \end{aligned}$$

It is worth noting here that, while $\bar{x} = 1/k$,

$$pr\left\{x \leq \frac{1}{k}\right\} = \int_0^{1/k} ke^{-kx}\, dx = -e^{-kx}\Big|_0^{1/k} = 1 - e^{-1} = .63+.$$

This should dispel any false notions that $pr\{x \leq \bar{x}\}$ ought to be $\frac{1}{2}$. The expectation has many important properties, but this is not one of them. For a continuous case (such as we have here) the number α such that $pr\{x \leq \alpha\} = \frac{1}{2}$ is called the *median* of the distribution. In the case of the radium atom this is found as follows:

$$\int_0^\alpha ke^{-kx}\,dx = 1 - e^{-ka} = \tfrac{1}{2};$$
$$e^{-ka} = \tfrac{1}{2};$$
$$\alpha = \frac{\log 2}{k} = \bar{x}\log 2.$$

44. Expectations

We saw in Chap. 5 that, if x is a stochastic variable, then in general $u = u(x)$ is also a stochastic variable. So u has an expectation given by Definition 1:

$$E(u) = \int_{-\infty}^{\infty} ug(u)du,$$

where $g(u)$ is the density function for u. We spent quite some time in Chap. 5 finding these density functions from the original density function $f(x)$. However, this sometimes turns out to be quite a chore, and one of the nicest things about expectations is that we do not have to find $g(u)$ in order to find $E(u)$. This observation holds for functions of several stochastic variables as well as for functions of one. A general statement might be given as follows:

Theorem I. If the stochastic variables $x_1, x_2, \ldots, x_n$ have a joint density function (joint probability function) $\varphi(x_1, x_2, \ldots, x_n)$ and if $u = u(x_1, x_2, \ldots, x_n)$ is any stochastic variable defined over the event space of the x's, then

$$E(u) = \int_{-\infty}^{\infty}\int_{-\infty}^{\infty} \cdots \int_{-\infty}^{\infty} u(x_1, x_2, \ldots, x_n)\varphi(x_1, x_2, \ldots, x_n)dx_1\,dx_2$$
$$\cdots dx_n$$
$$\left[E(u) = \sum_{x_1}\sum_{x_2} \cdots \sum_{x_n} u(x_1, x_2, \ldots, x_n)\varphi(x_1, x_2 \ldots, x_n). \right]$$

Important as this theorem is, we shall not try to give a general proof of it. Fundamentally, it involves the relationship between $g(u)$ and $\varphi(x_1, x_2, \ldots, x_n)$. In Theorems I to IV, Chap. 5, we got about as much information on this relationship as we can get in an elementary course. Our treatment of Theorem I will be to show what can be done on the basis of these four statements in Chap. 5. The student should bear in mind that, while our proof is incomplete, Theorem I is true in general.

First, let us take the discrete case. By definition

$$E(u) = \sum_u ug(u).$$

By Theorem I, Chap. 5,

$$g(a) = pr\{u = a\} = \sum_{u=a} \varphi(x_1, x_2, \ldots, x_n).$$

So

$$E(u) = \sum_a a \sum_{u=a} \varphi(x_1, x_2, \ldots, x_n).$$

This is the sum of all terms $u\varphi$, grouped according to the values of u. Now, the sum called for in Theorem I,

$$\sum_{x_1} \sum_{x_2} \cdots \sum_{x_n} u(x_1, x_2, \ldots, x_n)\varphi(x_1, x_2, \ldots, x_n),$$

is the sum of exactly the same terms; only this time they are grouped according to the values of the x's. Therefore, one sum is merely a rearrangement of the other. In the case of a finite sum, these are obviously equal. In the case of an infinite series, the requirement of absolute convergence guarantees that the rearrangement of the terms does not change the sum.

In the simplest continuous case (that covered by Theorem II, Chap. 5), the proof of Theorem I amounts to a simple change of variable. First, let us recall that in this case both $u(x)$ and its inverse are single-valued. Furthermore, $x'(u)$ has the same sign for all u's; that is, $|x'(u)| = \pm x'(u)$—the same sign applying everywhere. Starting, now, from the definition of expectation and applying Theorem II, Chap. 5, we have

$$E(u) = \int_{-\infty}^{\infty} u g(u) du$$

$$= \int_{-\infty}^{\infty} u f[x(u)]|x'(u)| du$$

$$= \int_{\mp\infty}^{\pm\infty} u f[x(u)] x'(u) du,$$

the limits of integration being reversed if x' is negative and remaining the same if x' is positive. Now, the substitution $u = u(x)$ either reverses the limits of integration again or leaves them alone, according to the same criteria; therefore

$$\int_{-\infty}^{\infty} u f[x(u)]|x'(u)| du = \int_{-\infty}^{\infty} u(x)f(x)dx.$$

Let us now abandon the idea of proving Theorem I and turn to some examples that illustrate that it really does work in cases covered by Theorems III and IV, Chap. 5. We saw in Sec. 39 that, if

$$\varphi(x,y) = \frac{1}{2\pi} e^{-(x^2+y^2)/2}$$

and $r = \sqrt{x^2 + y^2}$, then
$$f(r) = re^{-r^2/2}.$$
Therefore, by definition
$$E(r) = \int_0^\infty r^2 e^{-r^2/2}\, dr.$$
By Theorem I
$$E(r) = \int_{-\infty}^\infty \int_{-\infty}^\infty \frac{1}{2\pi} \sqrt{x^2 + y^2}\, e^{-(x^2+y^2)/2}\, dx\, dy.$$

To reduce the latter to the former, all we have to do is change to polar coordinates:
$$E(r) = \int_0^{2\pi} \int_0^\infty \frac{1}{2\pi}\, re^{-r^2/2}\, r\, dr\, d\theta$$
$$= \int_\pi^\infty \int_0^{2\pi} \frac{r^2}{2\pi}\, e^{-r^2/2}\, d\theta\, dr$$
$$= \int_0^\infty r^2\, e^{-r^2/2}\, dr.$$

To illustrate the cases covered by Theorem IV, Chap. 5, let us take a very simple example. Let
$$f(x) = \begin{cases} \tfrac{1}{2} & \text{for } -1 \le x \le 1, \\ 0 & \text{otherwise,} \end{cases}$$
and let
$$u = x^2.$$
By Theorem IV, Chap. 5,
$$g(u) = 2 \cdot \frac{1}{2} \cdot \frac{1}{2\sqrt{u}} = \frac{1}{2\sqrt{u}}.$$

(Note that we doubled it to take care of both branches.) So, by definition,
$$E(u) = \int_0^1 \frac{\sqrt{u}}{2}\, du = \frac{1}{3}\, u^{3/2} \Big|_0^1 = \frac{1}{3}.$$
By Theorem I,
$$E(u) = \int_{-1}^1 \frac{1}{2}\, x^2\, dx = \frac{1}{6}\, x^3 \Big|_{-1}^1 = \frac{1}{3}.$$

The formulas in Theorem I are often given as a definition of expectation. This is certainly the easy way out, because Theorem I gives the form from which expectations are ordinarily computed; and using it as a definition seemingly eliminates the necessity for all explanations. However, without Theorem I, such a definition is ambiguous. From the considerations in Chap. 5, we see that a given stochastic variable can be represented in many different ways as a function over first one event space and then another. From which representation is the expectation defined? According to Theorem I, they all lead to the same thing.

There are four immediate corollaries of Theorem I that are worth noting. If u is a stochastic variable and a is a constant,

Corollary 1
$$E(u + a) = E(u) + a.$$

Corollary 2
$$E(au) = aE(u).$$

Corollary 3
$$\text{var}(u) = E[(u - \bar{u})^2].$$

Corollary 4
$$E(u - \bar{u}) = 0.$$

By setting up the expectations of the sum and product of two stochastic variables in the form given by Theorem I, we obtain very easily two theorems which are invaluable in any work with moments. As usual, we shall base our proof on the assumption that there is a joint density function. We should point out, however, that Theorems II and III hold for any joint distribution for which the required expectations are defined.

Theorem II. If x and y are any two stochastic variables,

$$E(x + y) = E(x) + E(y).$$

This proof is very simple.

$$\begin{aligned}
E(x + y) &= \int_{-\infty}^{\infty} \int_{-\infty}^{\infty} (x + y)\varphi(x,y)dx\, dy \\
&= \int_{-\infty}^{\infty} x \int_{-\infty}^{\infty} \varphi(x,y)dy\, dx + \int_{-\infty}^{\infty} y \int_{-\infty}^{\infty} \varphi(x,y)dx\, dy \\
&= \int_{-\infty}^{\infty} xf(x)dx + \int_{-\infty}^{\infty} yg(y)dy \\
&= E(x) + E(y).
\end{aligned}$$

Repeated application of Theorem II, along with Corollary 2 to Theorem I, gives

Corollary 1. If $x_1, x_2, \ldots, x_n$ are stochastic variables and $a_1, a_2, \ldots, a_n$ are constants,

$$E\left(\sum_{i=1}^{n} a_i x_i\right) = \sum_{i=1}^{n} a_i E(x_i).$$

Theorem III. If x and y are independent stochastic variables,

$$E(xy) = E(x)E(y).$$

The proof of this is even simpler. If x and y are independent, $\varphi(x,y) = f(x)g(y)$; so

$$E(xy) = \int_{-\infty}^{\infty} \int_{-\infty}^{\infty} xy f(x)g(y)dx\,dy$$
$$= \int_{-\infty}^{\infty} x f(x)dx \int_{-\infty}^{\infty} y g(y)dy$$
$$= E(x)E(y).$$

A similar theorem holds for n variables, provided that they are totally independent. The student should note that this is a much stronger restriction than a requirement that every pair of them be independent.

It is very important to note that the addition theorem (Theorem II) holds for *all* pairs of stochastic variables, while in the multiplication theorem (Theorem III) we assumed *independence* of x and y. As we shall see later in this chapter, independence is not necessary for the multiplication theorem to hold; but it very definitely does not hold for all pairs of variables.

45. Example—Balls in an Urn

There are 3 balls in an urn, numbered 1, 2, 3. We draw 2 balls and note their numbers, then consider the expectation of the sum and product of the numbers noted. If we return the first ball before the second draw, the variables are independent; if we hold it out, they are not. Let us consider both cases. The joint and marginal probability functions are easily found in each case. They are as follows:

Independent case:

y	$g(y)$				
3	$\frac{1}{3}$	$\frac{1}{9}$	$\frac{1}{9}$	$\frac{1}{9}$	
2	$\frac{1}{3}$	$\frac{1}{9}$	$\frac{1}{9}$	$\frac{1}{9}$	
1	$\frac{1}{3}$	$\frac{1}{9}$	$\frac{1}{9}$	$\frac{1}{9}$	
		$\frac{1}{3}$	$\frac{1}{3}$	$\frac{1}{3}$	$f(x)$
		1	2	3	x

Dependent case:

y	$g(y)$			
3	⅓	⅙	⅙	0
2	⅓	⅙	0	⅙
1	⅓	0	⅙	⅙
		⅓	⅓	⅓	$f(x)$
		1	2	3	x

All the marginal probability functions are the same; so in each case

$$E(x) = E(y) = \tfrac{1}{3}(1 + 2 + 3) = 2.$$

Let us find the expectations of $x + y$ and xy from their probability functions. To get these, we draw the level lines for $x + y$ and xy:

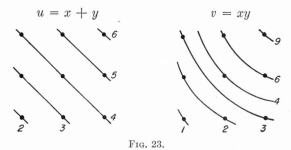

$$u = x + y \qquad\qquad v = xy$$

Fig. 23.

According to Theorem I, Chap. 5, the probability functions for u and v are obtained by adding the values of $\varphi(x,y)$ along these lines. So we have:

Independent case:

u:	2	3	4	5	6
$f(u)$:	⅑	²⁄₉	³⁄₉	²⁄₉	⅑

$$E(u) = \tfrac{1}{9}(2 + 6 + 12 + 10 + 6) = {}^{36}\!\!/_9 = 4.$$

v:	1	2	3	4	6	9
$g(v)$:	⅑	²⁄₉	²⁄₉	⅑	²⁄₉	⅑

$$E(v) = \tfrac{1}{9}(1 + 4 + 6 + 4 + 12 + 9) = {}^{36}\!\!/_9 = 4.$$

Dependent case:

u:	2	3	4	5	6
$f(u)$:	0	²⁄₆	²⁄₆	²⁄₆	0

$$E(u) = \tfrac{1}{6}(0 + 6 + 8 + 10 + 0) = {}^{24}\!\!/_6 = 4.$$

v:	1	2	3	4	6	9
$g(v)$:	0	²⁄₆	²⁄₆	0	²⁄₆	0

$$E(v) = \tfrac{1}{6}(0 + 4 + 6 + 0 + 12 + 0) = {}^{22}\!\!/_6.$$

Perhaps the educational thing about this example is not that the multiplication theorem fails in the dependent case but that the addition theorem holds in *both* cases. The student should note that this is not mere coincidence. It is a direct consequence of Theorem II.

46. Example—The Matching Problem

To illustrate the real power of Theorem II, let us consider a more complicated example. In Sec. 33 we saw that, if n numbered balls are placed in n numbered pockets, the probability that r of the numbers on the balls match the numbers on the pockets is

$$\frac{1}{r!} \sum_{s=0}^{n-r} \frac{(-1)^s}{s!}.$$

By definition, the expectation of the number of matchings is

$$E(r) = \sum_{r=0}^{n} \frac{r}{r!} \sum_{s=0}^{n-r} \frac{(-1)^s}{s!}.$$

A direct computation of this would be rather messy. However, the total number of matchings is the sum of the number of matchings for the individual balls. Now, each ball matches either once or not at all, and (*with no knowledge of what the other balls are doing*) we see that the probability of matching for each ball is $1/n$. Letting x_i ($i = 1, 2, \ldots, n$) be a stochastic variable assuming the values 0 and 1 with probability $1 - (1/n)$ and $1/n$, respectively, we have

$$E(x_i) = \frac{1}{n}$$

($i = 1, 2, \ldots, n$) and

$$r = \sum_{i=1}^{n} x_i,$$

whence

$$E(r) = \sum_{i=1}^{n} E(x_i) = n \cdot \frac{1}{n} = 1.$$

The variables x_i are obviously dependent here, but that does not affect the validity of our application of Theorem II.

A very interesting observation suggested by the above analysis of the matching problem concerns the experiments to test for extrasensory perception. Cards numbered from 1 to n are shuffled and then turned up one at a time. The supposedly gifted subject is placed so that he cannot see the cards, and as they are turned, he attempts to call off the numbers. Suppose a card is discarded after being turned so that, in a given run of n trials, each number appears once and only once. Suppose, further, that the subject knows this and tries to use cleverness as well as extrasensory perception by calling each number once and only once. Then, except for E.S.P., we have exactly the matching problem; and the expectation of the number of correct calls is 1.

However, the fascinating thing about this problem is that we get the same expectation no matter how the cards are handled and no matter how the subject organizes his calls. The number of correct calls in n trials is the sum of the number of correct calls on the individual trials. Therefore, Theorem II applies; and so long as the probability of success is $1/n$ on each trial, the expectation is exactly 1 on n trials no matter what the nature and degree of the dependence of the trials may be. Note, further, that $n \cdot (1/n) = 1$ for all n's; so it does not even matter how many cards are used!

47. Variance

The first thing we might note about the quantity var(x) is that, according to Corollary 3 to Theorem I, it is the expectation of a stochastic variable. Therefore, Theorem I applies to give us the result that, if x has a density function $f(x)$ and $u(x)$ is a stochastic variable over the x axis, then

$$\text{var}(u) = \int_{-\infty}^{\infty} [u(x) - \bar{u}]^2 f(x) dx.$$

For example, in the radium atom problem

$$f(u) = \begin{cases} ke^{-ku} & \text{for } u \geq 0, \\ 0 & \text{for } u < 0. \end{cases}$$

So

$$\text{var}(u) = \int_{0}^{\infty} k\left(u - \frac{1}{k}\right)^2 e^{-ku} \, du.$$

(see Sec. 43). However, in Chap. 5, we characterized the variable u as the function

$$u(x) = -\frac{1}{k} \log(1 - x)$$

over the unit interval with constant density function. We noted there that

$$\left(u - \frac{1}{k}\right)^2 = \frac{1}{k^2} \left[\log(1 - x) + 1\right]^2;$$

therefore

$$\operatorname{var}(u) = \int_0^1 \frac{1}{k^2} \left[\log(1 - x) + 1\right]^2 dx.$$

Finally, we saw that the variable

$$v = \left(u - \frac{1}{k}\right)^2$$

has a density function

$$g(v) = \begin{cases} 0 & \text{for } v < 0, \\ \dfrac{k}{e \sqrt{v}} \cosh(k \sqrt{v}) & \text{for } 0 \le v \le \dfrac{1}{k^2}, \\ \dfrac{k}{2 \sqrt{v}} e^{-k\sqrt{v}-1} & \text{for } v < \dfrac{1}{k^2}. \end{cases}$$

Therefore,

$$\operatorname{var}(u) = E(v) = \int_0^{1/k^2} \frac{k \sqrt{v}}{e} \cosh(k \sqrt{v}) dv + \int_{1/k^2}^{\infty} \frac{k \sqrt{v}}{2} e^{-k\sqrt{v}-1} dv.$$

Of these expressions for $\operatorname{var}(u)$, the first is obviously the simplest. We merely note the other two by way of pointing out that the points of view suggested by them are perfectly legitimate.

The characterization of $\operatorname{var}(x)$ as

$$E[(x - \bar{x})^2],$$

together with the addition and multiplication theorems for expectations, leads us to a number of interesting results.

Theorem IV. If x is a stochastic variable and a is a constant,

(a) $\operatorname{var}(x) = E(x^2) - \bar{x}^2.$

(b) $\operatorname{var}(x + a) = \operatorname{var}(x).$

(c) $\operatorname{var}(ax) = a^2 \operatorname{var}(x).$

These results follow immediately from the addition theorem and from the corollaries to Theorem I. To prove (a):

$$\begin{aligned} \operatorname{var}(x) &= E[(x - \bar{x})^2] = E(x^2 - 2x\bar{x} + \bar{x}^2) \\ &= E(x^2) - 2\bar{x}E(x) + \bar{x}^2 = E(x^2) - 2\bar{x}^2 + \bar{x}^2 \\ &= E(x^2) - \bar{x}^2. \end{aligned}$$

For (b), $E(x + a) = \bar{x} + a$; therefore

$$\text{var}(x + a) = E[(x + a - \bar{x} - a)^2] = E[(x - \bar{x})^2] = \text{var}(x).$$

For (c), $E(ax) = a\bar{x}$; therefore

$$\begin{aligned} \text{var}(ax) &= E[(ax - a\bar{x})^2] = E[a^2(x - \bar{x})^2] \\ &= a^2 E[(x - \bar{x})^2] = a^2\, \text{var}(x). \end{aligned}$$

The student would do well to remember (b) and (c) in particular. They say that a translation does not affect the variance, while a change of scale multiplies the variance by the square of the change of scale factor.

Theorem V.   If $x_1, x_2, \ldots, x_n$ are independent stochastic variables,

$$\text{var}\left(\sum_{i=1}^{n} x_i \right) = \sum_{i=1}^{n} \text{var}(x_i).$$

Let $z_i = x_i - \bar{x}_i$. Then, by Corollary 4 of Theorem I, $\bar{z}_i = 0$; so, by Theorem II,

$$E(\Sigma z_i) = 0.$$

Furthermore, by (b) of Theorem IV,

$$\text{var}(z_i) = \text{var}(x_i),$$

and since $\Sigma z_i = \Sigma(x_i - \bar{x}_i) = \Sigma x_i - \Sigma \bar{x}_i$,

$$\text{var}(\Sigma z_i) = \text{var}(\Sigma x_i).$$

Therefore, it suffices to prove that $\text{var}(\Sigma z_i) = \Sigma \text{var}(z_i)$. Since $E(\Sigma z_i) = 0$,

$$\begin{aligned} \text{var}\left(\sum_i z_i \right) &= E\left[\left(\sum_i z_i \right)^2 \right] \\ &= E\left(\sum_i z_i^2 + \sum_{i \neq j} z_i z_j \right) \\ &= \sum_i E(z_i^2) + \sum_{i \neq j} E(z_i z_j) \\ &= \sum_i \text{var}(z_i) + \sum_{i \neq j} E(z_i z_j). \end{aligned}$$

Now, since the x's are independent, the z's are too; so Theorem III applies, and

$$E(z_i z_j) = E(z_i)E(z_j) = 0$$

for $i \neq j$. This gives us the result we want.

The variance of a stochastic variable is supposed to give some indication of the "spread" of the values of the variable. An indication of the way in which it does this is given by the following:

Theorem VI (*Tshebysheff's Inequality*). If x is any stochastic variable and σ is its standard deviation, then

$$pr\{|x - \bar{x}| \geq t\sigma\} \leq \frac{1}{t^2}.$$

To simplify matters, let $z = x - \bar{x}$. This does not alter the value of σ. Now, we have

$$\sigma^2 = \int_{-\infty}^{\infty} z^2 f(z)dz \geq \int_{|z| \geq t\sigma} z^2 f(z)dz$$

$$\geq \int_{|z| \geq t\sigma} (t\sigma)^2 f(z)dz$$

$$= t^2 \sigma^2 pr\{|z| \geq t\sigma\};$$

and, dividing by $t^2\sigma^2$, we have

$$\frac{1}{t^2} \geq pr\{|z| \geq t\sigma\}.$$

For each $t \geq 1$, there is a stochastic variable for which the equality in Tshebysheff's inequality holds. Consider, for instance, the variable

$x:$	$-t$	0	t
$f(x):$	$\dfrac{1}{2t^2}$	$1 - \left(\dfrac{1}{t^2}\right)$	$\dfrac{1}{2t^2}$

Here $\sigma = 1$, and $pr\{|x| = t\} = 1/t^2$.

In this sense Theorem VI is the best general estimate of its kind. However, to get an example of the equality, we should have to change the stochastic variable as we change t. Therefore, for a given stochastic variable, Theorem VI is by no means a best estimate for every value of t. Obviously, if we know the density or probability function for a stochastic variable, we do not need any estimate like Theorem VI at all. To get $pr\{|x - \bar{x}| \geq t\sigma\}$, we merely integrate (or add) over the indicated domain. In between these two extremes, there is the possibility that $f(x)$ is not definitely known but that there are some known restrictions on it. Several "improvements" on Tshebysheff's inequality have been proved by assuming such restrictive hypotheses, but we shall not attempt to summarize them here.

It might be interesting to compare the results given by Theorem VI with the actual values of $pr\{|x - \bar{x}| \geq t\sigma\}$ for the normal distribution.

	$pr\{|x - \bar{x}| \geq t\sigma\}$	
t	Upper limit for all distributions	Actual value for normal distribution
1	1.00	.3174
2	.25	.0456
3	.11	.0027
4	.08	.00006

This table shows that Theorem VI does not even come close to giving an estimate of the probability significance of σ for a normal distribution. But this argument cuts both ways. Our table also shows that the normal distribution does not even come close to estimating the possible vagaries of a stochastic variable.

48. Example—Bernoullian Trials

In Chap. 4 we saw that a Bernoullian sequence of trials was represented by a sequence of stochastic variables:

$$x_i: \quad 0 \quad 1$$
$$f_i(x_i): \quad q \quad p$$

For each i,

$$E(x_i) = 0 \cdot q + 1 \cdot p = p.$$

The number of successes in n trials we have denoted by r. We have seen that

$$r = \sum_{i=1}^{n} x_i.$$

Therefore, by Theorem II,

$$E(r) = \Sigma E(x_i) = np.$$

For each i, the variance of x_i is

$$E(x_i^2) - \bar{x}_i^2 = (0 \cdot q + 1 \cdot p) - p^2 = p(1 - p) = pq.$$

The variables are independent; so Theorem V applies, and

$$\text{var}(r) = \Sigma \text{var}(x_i) = npq.$$

The student should make a note of these results. They will be needed frequently in later chapters. As we pointed out in our discussion of extrasensory perception tests (see example on the matching problem earlier in this chapter), the expectation of the number of successes is np no matter how the trials are related. The thing that makes the study of Bernoullian trials particularly profitable is that for them we have such a simple expression for the variance of the number of successes.

49. Covariance and Correlation

If x and y are stochastic variables, the variance of each of them is the expectation of the square of its deviation from its mean. The *covariance* of the two is defined as the expectation of the product of their deviations from their respective means. That is,

$$\operatorname{covar}(x,y) = E[(x - \bar{x})(y - \bar{y})].$$

Now, it follows immediately from the addition theorem (Theorem II) that

$$\operatorname{covar}(x,y) = E(xy - \bar{x}y - x\bar{y} + \bar{x}\bar{y})$$
$$= E(xy) - E(x)E(y).$$

If $\operatorname{covar}(x,y) = 0$, we say that x and y are *uncorrelated*. The following theorem is now obvious.

Theorem VII.   A necessary and sufficient condition that

$$E(xy) = E(x)E(y)$$

is that x and y be uncorrelated.

On comparing Theorems VII and III, we have the following:

Corollary 1.   If x and y are independent, they are uncorrelated.

The converse to Corollary 1 is not true. Variables may be uncorrelated but badly dependent. For example, if x is a variable with a constant density function $f(x) = \frac{1}{2}$ on $-1 \leq x \leq 1$ and if $y = x^2$, then

$$E(x) = \int_{-1}^{1} \frac{1}{2}x \, dx = 0;$$

so

$$E(x)E(y) = 0.$$

Furthermore,

$$E(xy) = \int_{-1}^{1} \frac{1}{2}x^3 \, dx = 0;$$

thus x and y are uncorrelated. However, for each value of x, there is only one possible value for y; and for each value of y, there are only two possible values for x. Therefore, x and y are far from being independent.

The importance of uncorrelated variables in probability theory is that in many instances we want to be able to write $E(x)E(y)$ for $E(xy)$. In these instances it is sufficient to postulate that x and y are uncorrelated. Theorems depending on this maneuver will obviously hold if x and y are independent, but it is probably a good idea to use the weaker hypothesis when possible. This not only gives a theoretically stronger theorem but frequently makes the hypotheses easier to verify in specific instances.

A further pertinent observation is that if x, y, and z are *uncorrelated by pairs*, i.e., if

$$\mathrm{covar}(x,y) = \mathrm{covar}(x,z) = \mathrm{covar}(y,z) = 0,$$

it does not follow that

$$E(xyz) = E(x)E(y)E(z).$$

In Chap. 3 we made an analogous observation with regard to independence of stochastic variables, and the example given there (page 48) demonstrates our present point too. In that example the variables are independent by pairs, therefore uncorrelated by pairs; yet

$$E(xyz) = \tfrac{1}{4},$$

while

$$E(x)E(y)E(z) = \tfrac{1}{2} \times \tfrac{1}{2} \times \tfrac{1}{2} = \tfrac{1}{8}.$$

In the proof of Theorem V we used the hypothesis of independence only to justify the use of the multiplication theorem. Furthermore, we applied the multiplication theorem to only two variables at a time. Therefore, it follows from Theorem VII that in this theorem, "uncorrelated by pairs" will suffice in place of "independent." For future reference, let us restate the theorem in this stronger form.

Corollary 2. If x_1, x_2, . . . , x_n are stochastic variables which are uncorrelated by pairs, then

$$\mathrm{var}(\Sigma x_i) = \Sigma \, \mathrm{var}(x_i).$$

The statistician uses covariance in connection with the *coefficient of linear correlation* of two stochastic variables:

$$r = \frac{\mathrm{covar}(x,y)}{[\mathrm{var}(x) \, \mathrm{var}(y)]^{1/2}}.$$

In case $x - \bar{x}$ and $y - \bar{y}$ are linearly dependent, *i.e.*, if

$$y - \bar{y} = k(x - \bar{x}),$$

then, letting $u = x - \bar{x}$ and $v = y - \bar{y}$, we have

$$r = \frac{E(ku^2)}{[E(u^2)E(k^2u^2)]^{\frac{1}{2}}} = \frac{kE(u^2)}{[k^2E(u^2)E(u^2)]^{\frac{1}{2}}} = \frac{k}{|k|} = \pm 1,$$

the sign of r being the same as that of k. The converse is also true; *i.e.*, if $|r| = 1$, then $y - \bar{y} = k(x - \bar{x})$. We shall not go into the proof of this, but we should show that in all cases $|r| \leq 1$.

Theorem VIII (*Schwarz's Inequality*). For any stochastic variables x and y,

$$[E(xy)]^2 \leq E(x^2)E(y^2).$$

For every real constant α, the variable $(\alpha x - y)^2$ is always nonnegative and therefore has a nonnegative expectation. That is,

$$\alpha^2 E(x^2) - 2\alpha E(xy) + E(y^2) \geq 0$$

for every α. In particular, this holds for

$$\alpha = \frac{E(xy)}{E(x^2)};$$

and on substituting this value for α, we have

$$\frac{[E(xy)]^2}{E(x^2)} - \frac{2[E(xy)]^2}{E(x^2)} + E(y^2) \geq 0.$$

The result now follows if we multiply by $E(x^2)$ and transpose.

To apply Theorem VIII to the correlation coefficient, all we have to do is to translate the origin of each variable to its mean; then we substitute into Theorem VIII, divide by $E(x^2)E(y^2)$, and take square roots. The resulting inequality is just exactly $|r| \leq 1$.

50. Normal Correlation

There is one very important case in which the coefficient of linear correlation gives considerably more information than we have suggested so far. If x and y have the joint density function postulated in Theorem IX below, they are said to be in *normal correlation*. Such variables appear in many different connections, and we want to develop here a few of their more important properties.

Theorem IX. If x and y have the joint density function

$$\varphi(x,y) = \frac{1}{2\pi\sigma_1\sigma_2\sqrt{1-r^2}}\exp\left[-\frac{1}{2(1-r^2)}\left(\frac{x^2}{\sigma_1^2}-\frac{2rxy}{\sigma_1\sigma_2}+\frac{y^2}{\sigma_2^2}\right)\right]$$

where $|r| < 1$, then each of the following statements holds:

(a) x is normally distributed with variance σ_1^2, and y is normally distributed with variance σ_2^2.

(b) There exist independent normally distributed variables u and v such that each of the variables x and y is a linear combination of u and v.

(c) The constant r in the above joint density function is the correlation coefficient of x and y.

(d) x and y are independent if and only if they are uncorrelated.

The proof of (a) consists in finding the marginal density functions. If we complete the square in the exponent of $\varphi(x,y)$, we get for an exponent

$$-\frac{1}{2(1-r^2)}\left[\left(\frac{y}{\sigma_2}-\frac{rx}{\sigma_1}\right)^2+(1-r^2)\frac{x^2}{\sigma_1^2}\right];$$

therefore

$$f(x) = \int_{-\infty}^{\infty}\varphi(x,y)dy$$

$$= \frac{1}{\sigma_1\sqrt{2\pi}}e^{-x^2/2\sigma_1^2}\int_{-\infty}^{\infty}\frac{1}{\sigma_2\sqrt{2\pi(1-r^2)}}\exp\left[-\frac{1}{2(1-r^2)}\left(\frac{y}{\sigma_2}-\frac{rx}{\sigma_1}\right)^2\right]dy$$

$$= \frac{1}{\sigma_1\sqrt{2\pi}}e^{-x^2/2\sigma_1^2}.$$

Similarly,

$$g(y) = \frac{1}{\sigma_2\sqrt{2\pi}}e^{-y^2/2\sigma_2^2};$$

and (a) is proved.

Actually, (b) follows immediately from considerations of analytic geometry. Independent normal variables u and v are characterized by a joint density function of the form

$$Ke^{-(a^2u^2+b^2v^2)}.$$

Now, a rotation of the axes always gives the old variables as linear combinations of the new, and there is always a rotation that will remove the cross-product term. Furthermore, the condition $|r| < 1$ makes the discriminant of the exponent negative:

$$\left(\frac{-2r}{\sigma_1\sigma_2}\right)^2 - 4 \cdot \frac{1}{\sigma_1^2} \cdot \frac{1}{\sigma_2^2} = 4 \cdot \frac{r^2 - 1}{\sigma_1^2\sigma_2^2} < 0;$$

so the rotation always leads to a sum of squares (equation of an ellipse). Clearly, a rigid transformation like a rotation carries the area differential $dx\ dy$ into $du\ dv$; so we get a new joint density function of the desired form, and (b) is proved.

In order to prove (c) we need to look a little more closely at the details of this rotation transformation. If α is the angle of rotation, we have the relations (found in any analytic geometry book):

(1)
$$x = u \cos \alpha - v \sin \alpha,$$
$$y = u \sin \alpha + v \cos \alpha.$$

(2)
$$u = x \cos \alpha + y \sin \alpha,$$
$$v = -x \sin \alpha + y \cos \alpha.$$

Furthermore, the rotation which removes the xy term in the exponent of $\varphi(x,y)$ is characterized by the condition

(3)
$$\tan 2\alpha = \frac{2r\ \sigma_1\sigma_2}{\sigma_1^2 - \sigma_2^2}.$$

From (1) we find that

$$xy = (u^2 - v^2) \sin \alpha \cos \alpha + uv(\cos^2 \alpha - \sin^2 \alpha)$$
$$= \tfrac{1}{2}(u^2 - v^2) \sin 2\alpha + uv \cos 2\alpha.$$

Now u and v are independent and normal; so $E(uv) = 0$. Therefore,

$$E(xy) = \tfrac{1}{2}E(u^2 - v^2) \sin 2\alpha.$$

From (2) we get

$$u^2 - v^2 = (x^2 - y^2)(\cos^2 \alpha - \sin^2 \alpha) + 4xy \sin \alpha \cos \alpha$$
$$= (x^2 - y^2) \cos 2\alpha + 2xy \sin 2\alpha;$$

so

$$E(xy) = \tfrac{1}{2}E(x^2 - y^2) \sin 2\alpha \cos 2\alpha + E(xy) \sin^2 2\alpha.$$

Transposing, we have

$$2E(xy)(1 - \sin^2 2\alpha) = E(x^2 - y^2) \sin 2\alpha \cos 2\alpha;$$

that is,

$$2E(xy) \cos^2 2\alpha = [E(x^2) - E(y^2)] \sin 2\alpha \cos 2\alpha$$
$$= (\sigma_1^2 - \sigma_2^2) \sin 2\alpha \cos 2\alpha$$

Therefore,

$$E(xy) = \tfrac{1}{2}(\sigma_1^2 - \sigma_2^2) \tan 2\alpha;$$

so by (3)

$$E(xy) = r\sigma_1\sigma_2.$$

This proves (c).

At this stage, (d) is obvious. The joint density function $\varphi(x,y)$ reduces to the form for independent variables if and only if $r = 0$.

One final remark of interest about variables in normal correlation is that the loci

$$\frac{x^2}{\sigma_1^2} - \frac{2rxy}{\sigma_1\sigma_2} + \frac{y^2}{\sigma_2^2} = \text{constant}$$

are called (for obvious reasons) the ellipses of equal probability. Equation (3) shows how the orientation of the axes of these ellipses can be determined from the standard deviations σ_1 and σ_2 and the correlation coefficient r.

REFERENCES FOR FURTHER STUDY

Coolidge, *An Introduction to Mathematical Probability*, Chap. VIII.
Levy and Roth, *Elements of Probability*, Chap. VIII.
Uspensky, *Introduction to Mathematical Probability*, Chaps. IX, XV.

PROBLEMS

1. Five dice are tossed together, the experiment being repeated 216 times. What is the expectation of the number of times exactly 3 aces appear? *Ans.* $125/18$.

2. The face cards are discarded from 2 decks of cards; then 1 card is drawn from each deck. What is the expectation of the sum of the numbers drawn? *Ans.* 11.

3. Two cards are drawn simultaneously from 1 of the decks in Prob. 2. What is the expectation of the sum? *Ans.* 11.

4. Thirteen cards are drawn simultaneously from a deck of 52. If aces count 1, face cards 10, and others according to denomination, find the expectation of the total score on the 13 cards. *Ans.* 85.

5. There are 1,000 tickets in a certain lottery, numbered 1 to 1,000. If 30 different winners are picked, what is the expectation of the sum of the winning numbers? *Ans.* 15,015.

6. What is the expectation of the total thrown on 2 dice? on n dice? *Ans.* $7, 7n/2$.

7. What is the standard deviation of the total thrown on n dice? *Ans.* $\sqrt{35n/12}$.

8. If x is chosen at random in the interval (a,b), what is $E(x)$? $\text{var}(x)$? *Ans.* $(a+b)/2, (b-a)^2/12$.

9. Let x and y be chosen independently and at random between 0 and 1.   Find the expectation and variance of $x + y$.   *Ans.*   1, $\frac{1}{6}$.

10. If x is normally distributed with variance unity, what is the expectation of x^2? the variance of x^2?   *Ans.* 1, 2.

11. If $x_1, x_2, \ldots, x_n$ are independent and if each is normally distributed with unit variance, what is the expectation of Σx_i^2? the variance of Σx_i^2?   *Ans.* n, $2n$.

12. A Poisson sequence of trials is a sequence of independent trials in which (unlike the Bernoullian case) the probability of success varies from trial to trial.   Let the probability of success on the ith trial be p_i (failure, q_i), and let p be the mean probability in n trials:

$$p = \frac{1}{n} \sum_{i=1}^{n} p_i.$$

Show that the expectation of the number of successes in n trials is np and the variance of the number of successes is

$$\sum_{i=1}^{n} p_i q_i.$$

13. Two dice are thrown until a 7 is thrown.   Find the most probable number of throws and the expectation of the number of throws.
Ans. 1, 6.

14. Let x have a Poisson distribution; that is, $x = 0, 1, 2, 3, \ldots$ with a probability function $f(x) = a^x e^{-a}/x!$.   Show that

$$E(x^2) = aE(x + 1).$$

15. Find the expectation and variance of a variable with the Poisson distribution.   *Ans.* a, a.

16. *St. Petersburg Problem.*   A player tosses a coin.   If his first toss is heads, he wins a dollar.   If his second toss is heads, he wins another dollar.   For a third straight heads he gets an additional two dollars. As long as a run lasts, his winnings are doubled each time he tosses another heads.   Any time he tosses a tails, the game is over.   Find the expectation of the amount paid him in a single game.   *Ans.* ∞.

17. Since the game in Prob. 16 seems impractical, suppose that, once his winnings reach \$1,000,000 by the rules of Prob. 16, the player receives \$1,000,000 for each additional heads instead of having his winnings doubled each time.   What is the expectation of the amount won under these rules?   *Ans.*   10.96.

18. Let x and y be independent and normally distributed, each with variance unity. Find the expectation and variance of $\sqrt{x^2 + y^2}$.
$$Ans. \quad \sqrt{\pi/2}, \; 2 - (\pi/2).$$

19. Let x be normally distributed with variance unity. Find the expectation of $|x|$. $\qquad\qquad Ans. \quad \sqrt{2/\pi}.$

20. Let x be normally distributed with variance unity. Find the expectation and variance of e^{ax}. $\qquad Ans. \quad e^{a^2/2}, \; e^{2a^2} - e^{a^2}.$

21. A variable x with the density function

$$f(x) = \frac{1}{x\sqrt{2\pi}} e^{-(\log x)^2/2} \qquad\qquad (x > 0)$$

is said to have a logarithmiconormal distribution. Find the expectation and variance of this variable. Hint: Compare Prob. 20 above with Prob. 24, Chap. 5. $\qquad\qquad Ans. \quad \sqrt{e}, \; e^2 - e.$

22. Let x have a density function $f(x) = \frac{1}{2}e^{-|x|}$. Find the expectation and variance of x. $\qquad\qquad Ans. \quad 0, \; 2.$

23. Pareto's distribution is defined by the density function

$$f(x) = \begin{cases} \dfrac{\alpha}{x_0}\left(\dfrac{x_0}{x}\right)^{\alpha+1} & \text{for } x > x_0, \\ 0 & \text{for } x \le x_0. \end{cases}$$

Show that a variable with this distribution has a moment of order k if and only if $\alpha > k$. In particular, if $\alpha > 1$, show that

$$E(x) = \alpha x_0/(\alpha - 1).$$

24. Generalize (a) of Theorem IV. If a is any constant

$$\text{var}(x) = E[(x - a)^2] - [E(x - a)]^2.$$

25. Show from Prob. 24 that the mean of a variable is the point about which its mean square deviation is a minimum.

26. Use the method of proof of Theorem VI to show that, if x is a stochastic variable whose density function is zero for $x < 0$, then, for $t > 0$, $pr\{x \ge t\} \le \bar{x}/t$.

27. Show that Theorem VI is a special case of the theorem in Prob. 26.

28. Show that for any pair of stochastic variables

$$\text{var}(x + y) = \text{var}(x) + \text{var}(y) + 2\,\text{covar}(x,y).$$

29. Generalize Prob. 28. If $x_1, x_2, \ldots, x_n$ is any set of n stochastic variables,

$$\text{var}\left(\sum_i x_i\right) = \sum_i \text{var}(x_i) + \sum_{i \ne j} \text{covar}(x_i, y_j).$$

30. Find the coefficient of correlation of the variables in Prob. 31, Chap. 3.   *Ans.* 0.

31. If the joint density function for x and y is $\varphi(x,y) = x + y$ ($0 \leq x \leq 1, 0 \leq y \leq 1$) with $\varphi = 0$ otherwise, what is the correlation coefficient for x and y?   *Ans.* $-\frac{1}{11}$.

32. Let x and y be chosen independently and at random between 0 and 1. Find the correlation coefficient for $u = \max.(x,y)$ and $v = \min.(x,y)$.   Hint: See Probs. 11 to 13, Chap. 5.   *Ans.* $\frac{1}{2}$.

33. Show that, if x is chosen at random between $-\pi$ and π, sin mx and sin nx are uncorrelated when $m \neq n$.

34. Show that, if x and y are in normal correlation, then ax and by are in normal correlation.

35. For x and y in normal correlation and independent, what is the orientation of the ellipse of equal probability?

36. Experience shows that in artillery fire the pattern of hits forms an approximately normal distribution with the major axis of the ellipse of equal probability on the line from gun to target. Given a record of a large number of hits from the same gun in a given area, show how Equation (3), Sec. 50, can be used to determine approximately the direction from there to the gun.

CHAPTER 7

SPECIAL TOPICS IN CALCULUS

There are a number of special formulas and identities which are not usually included in a first course in calculus but which are very useful tools in many computations in probability theory. It is the purpose of this chapter to summarize these. In later portions of this book we shall make a number of references to the formulas developed here, but we shall not begin to indicate all the uses that can be made of this material. The student who is interested in further work in probability and statistics would do well to make the information presented in this chapter a part of his general repertory.

51. The Beta and Gamma Functions

The beta and gamma functions are sometimes called Eulerian integrals of the first and second kind, respectively. They are defined as follows:

$$(1) \qquad \mathrm{B}(x,y) = \int_0^1 t^{x-1}(1-t)^{y-1}\, dt;$$

$$(2) \qquad \Gamma(x) = \int_0^\infty t^{x-1}e^{-t}\, dt.$$

A little knowledge of improper integrals tells us immediately that $\mathrm{B}(x,y)$ is defined if x and y are both greater than zero and that $\Gamma(x)$ is defined if $x > 0$. In what follows, we shall understand that, whenever we write B or Γ, the arguments used satisfy these conditions.

On integrating (2) by parts, we get

$$\int_0^\infty t^{x-1}e^{-t}\, dt = -t^{x-1}e^{-t}\Big|_0^\infty + (x-1)\int_0^\infty t^{x-2}e^{-t}\, dt,$$

which gives us the important recursion formula:

$$(3) \qquad \Gamma(x) = (x-1)\Gamma(x-1).$$

So, starting with the special case

$$(4) \qquad \Gamma(1) = \int_0^\infty e^{-t}\, dt = 1,$$

we can apply (3) over and over again to find that $\Gamma(2) = 1$, $\Gamma(3) = 2$,

$\Gamma(4) = 6$, and in general

(5) $$\Gamma(n + 1) = n!.$$

This relation should suggest something of the importance of the gamma function.

In the integral (2) let us make the change of variable $t = av$ where a is a constant:

$$\Gamma(x) = \int_0^\infty a^{x-1}v^{x-1}e^{-av}a \, dv.$$

Factoring out a^x, we have another useful formula:

(6) $$\frac{\Gamma(x)}{a^x} = \int_0^\infty v^{x-1}e^{-av} \, dv.$$

Turning now to the beta integral (1), let us make the change of variable $t = 1 - s$. This gives us the important symmetry formula:

(7) $$\begin{aligned} B(x,y) &= \int_1^0 (1 - s)^{x-1}s^{y-1}(-ds) \\ &= \int_0^1 s^{y-1}(1 - s)^{x-1} \, ds \\ &= B(y,x). \end{aligned}$$

Returning to (1), we make the substitutions

$$t = \frac{u}{1 + u}, \qquad 1 - t = \frac{1}{1 + u}, \qquad dt = \frac{du}{(1 + u)^2}.$$

This gives

(8) $$B(x,y) = \int_0^\infty \frac{u^{x-1}}{(1 + u)^{x+y}} \, du.$$

From (6) we have

$$\int_0^\infty v^{x+y-1}e^{-(1+u)v} \, dv = \frac{\Gamma(x + y)}{(1 + u)^{x+y}}.$$

If we multiply each side by $u^{y-1} \, du$ and integrate with respect to u from 0 to ∞, we have

$$\int_0^\infty v^{x+y-1}e^{-v} \, dv \int_0^\infty u^{y-1}e^{-uv} \, du = \Gamma(x + y) \int_0^\infty \frac{u^{y-1}}{(1 + u)^{x+y}} \, du.$$

Applying (6) to the second integral on the left and (8) to the integral on the right, we get

$$\Gamma(y) \int_0^\infty v^{x-1}e^{-v} \, dv = \Gamma(x + y)B(y,x).$$

So, from (2) and (7), we get the important relation between B and Γ:

$$(9) \qquad\qquad B(x,y) = \frac{\Gamma(x)\Gamma(y)}{\Gamma(x+y)}.$$

If, in (9), we replace $B(x,y)$ by its integral expression (1) and make the change of variable

$$t = \cos^2 \theta, \qquad dt = 2 \cos \theta \sin \theta \, d\theta,$$

we have

$$\frac{\Gamma(x)\Gamma(y)}{\Gamma(x+y)} = 2 \int_0^{\pi/2} (\cos \theta)^{2x-1}(\sin \theta)^{2y-1} \, d\theta;$$

hence, setting $x = y = \frac{1}{2}$ and noting (4), we have

$$\frac{[\Gamma(\frac{1}{2})]^2}{\Gamma(1)} = \left[\Gamma\left(\frac{1}{2}\right)\right]^2 = 2 \int_0^{\pi/2} d\theta = \pi.$$

Thus,

$$(10) \qquad\qquad \Gamma(\tfrac{1}{2}) = \sqrt{\pi}.$$

On writing the integral (1) for $B(x,x)$:

$$B(x,x) = \int_0^1 t^{x-1}(1-t)^{x-1} \, dt,$$

we see that the integrand is symmetric about $t = \frac{1}{2}$; so we can write

$$B(x,x) = 2 \int_0^{\frac{1}{2}} t^{x-1}(1-t)^{x-1} \, dt.$$

The change of variable

$$t = \tfrac{1}{2}(1 - \sqrt{s}), \qquad t(1-t) = \tfrac{1}{4}(1-s), \qquad dt = -\tfrac{1}{4}s^{-\frac{1}{2}} \, ds$$

then gives

$$B(x,x) = 2^{1-2x} \int_0^1 (1-s)^{x-1}s^{-\frac{1}{2}} \, ds$$
$$= 2^{1-2x}B(x,\tfrac{1}{2}).$$

If, in this equation, we transform the beta functions into gamma functions by means of (9), we have the formula of Legendre:

$$(11) \qquad\qquad \Gamma(2x)\Gamma(\tfrac{1}{2}) = 2^{2x-1}\Gamma(x)\Gamma(x + \tfrac{1}{2}).$$

52. The O, o Notation

A very useful tool in analysis is the so-called "big O" and "little o" notation. If $y = y(x)$ and some limit operation for x is understood (say, $x \to \infty$), then $o(y)$ is used to denote a function $z(x)$ such that

$$\lim \frac{z}{y} = 0.$$

$O(y)$ is used to denote a function $z(x)$ such that z/y is bounded for x sufficiently large. These are generic notations and do not denote specific functions. This makes them very useful for describing remainder terms whose specific values we do not care about but whose asymptotic behavior is important.

In particular, $o(1)$ means a function which tends to zero. Several special properties of $o(1)$ functions should be pointed out. First, the sum or difference of $o(1)$'s is $o(1)$. For exponentials and logarithms we have the relations

$$\log[1 + o(1)] = o(1);$$
$$e^{o(1)} = 1 + o(1).$$

The relation $f(x) \sim g(x)$ is an important one in analysis. It is read "$f(x)$ is asymptotic to $g(x)$" and means, by definition,

$$\lim \frac{f(x)}{g(x)} = 1.$$

Clearly, this may be written

$$f(x) = g(x)[1 + o(1)],$$

or

$$\log f = \log g + o(1).$$

We shall frequently be interested in the asymptotic behavior of expressions of the form $(x + a) \log(x + b)$ as $x \to \infty$. It will simplify matters if we figure this out and record the result now. From Maclaurin's formula with remainder, we find that

$$\log(1 + z) = z + O(z^2)$$

as $z \to 0$; therefore, as $x \to \infty$,

$$(x + a) \log(x + b) = (x + a) \log x \left(1 + \frac{b}{x}\right)$$
$$= (x + a) \log x + (x + a) \log \left(1 + \frac{b}{x}\right)$$
$$= (x + a) \log x + (x + a) \left[\frac{b}{x} + O(x^{-2})\right]$$
$$= (x + a) \log x + b + O(x^{-1}) + aO(x^{-1}).$$

So let us list for reference:

(1) $(x + a) \log(x + b) = x \log x + a \log x + b + o(1).$

The "big O" relationship is the thing involved in the comparison test for convergence of infinite series. Thus, one of our chief uses of it will be to note that, if $p > 1$,

$$\sum_{n=1}^{\infty} O\left(\frac{1}{n^p}\right)$$

is convergent.

53. Stirling's Theorem

There is a famous asymptotic formula for $n!$ which commonly goes under the name of Stirling's theorem, though it appears that a lot of the credit for it should go to de Moivre.

Theorem I.

$$n! = n^{n+\frac{1}{2}} e^{-n} \sqrt{2\pi}\, e^{\epsilon_n}$$

where

(1)
$$\frac{1}{12n + 6} < \epsilon_n < \frac{1}{12n}.$$

We shall prove this formula in its logarithmic form:

(2) $\log(n!) = (n + \frac{1}{2}) \log n - n + \frac{1}{2} \log(2\pi) + \epsilon_n.$

Now,

$$\log(n!) = \sum_{k=1}^{n} \log k.$$

If we draw a graph of $\log x$, we get a picture of this sum as the sum of areas of rectangles:

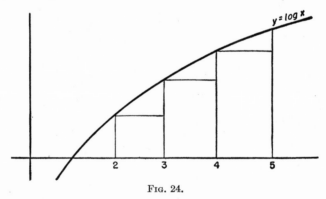

FIG. 24.

From this it appears that

$$\sum_{k=1}^{n} \log k$$

is approximately equal to

$$\int_{1}^{n+1} \log x\, dx.$$

However, we see that there is a closer approximation if we shift the rectangles $\frac{1}{2}$ unit to the left:

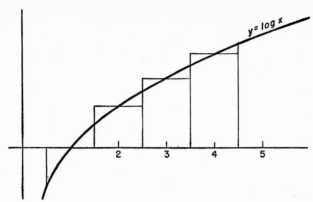

FIG. 25.

We shall use the approximation suggested by this figure, that is,

$$\log(n!) \simeq \int_{\frac{1}{2}}^{n+\frac{1}{2}} \log x \, dx.$$

First, however, let us find out how good an approximation it is. To do this, we note that

$$\int_{k-\frac{1}{2}}^{k+\frac{1}{2}} \log t \, dt = \int_{k}^{k+\frac{1}{2}} \log t \, dt - \int_{k}^{k-\frac{1}{2}} \log t \, dt.$$

In the first integral we make the change of variable

$$t = k + x, \qquad dt = dx;$$

in the second, we let

$$t = k - x, \qquad dt = -dx.$$

Then,

$$\begin{aligned}
\int_{k-\frac{1}{2}}^{k+\frac{1}{2}} \log t \, dt &= \int_{0}^{\frac{1}{2}} \log(k + x)dx + \int_{0}^{\frac{1}{2}} \log(k - x)dx \\
&= \int_{0}^{\frac{1}{2}} \log(k^2 - x^2)dx \\
&= \int_{0}^{\frac{1}{2}} \log\left[k^2\left(1 - \frac{x^2}{k^2}\right)\right] dx \\
&= \int_{0}^{\frac{1}{2}} 2 \log k \, dx + \int_{0}^{\frac{1}{2}} \log\left(1 - \frac{x^2}{k^2}\right) dx \\
&= \log k + \int_{0}^{\frac{1}{2}} \log\left(1 - \frac{x^2}{k^2}\right) dx.
\end{aligned}$$

Now, the series expansion

$$\log\left(1 - \frac{x^2}{k^2}\right) = -\frac{x^2}{k^2} - \frac{1}{2}\frac{x^4}{k^4} - \frac{1}{3}\frac{x^6}{k^6} - \cdots$$

is convergent for $x^2/k^2 < 1$; therefore we may integrate from 0 to $\frac{1}{2}$, term by term, and get

$$\int_0^{1/2} \log\left(1 - \frac{x^2}{k^2}\right) dx = -\frac{x^3}{3k^2} - \frac{x^5}{10k^4} - \cdots \Big|_0^{1/2}$$

$$= \frac{1}{k^2}\left(-\frac{1}{24} - \frac{1}{320k^2} - \cdots\right)$$

$$= O(k^{-2}).$$

Therefore,

$$\int_{k-1/2}^{k+1/2} \log t \, dt = \log k + O(k^{-2}),$$

and

$$\log(n!) = \sum_{k=1}^{n} \log k$$

$$= \sum_{k=1}^{n} \left[\int_{k-1/2}^{k+1/2} \log t \, dt + O(k^{-2}) \right]$$

$$= \int_{1/2}^{n+1/2} \log t \, dt + \sum_{k=1}^{n} O(k^{-2})$$

$$= t \log t - t \Big|_{1/2}^{n+1/2} + \sum_{k=1}^{\infty} O(k^{-2}) + o(1)$$

$$= (n + 1/2) \log(n + 1/2) - n + C_1 + o(1)$$

where the constant C_1 is $-1/2 \log(1/2) + \Sigma O(k^{-2})$. On applying
(1), Sec. 52, we get an additional constant term of $-1/2$; so letting
$C_2 = C_1 - 1/2$, we have

(3) $\log(n!) = (n + 1/2) \log n - n + C_2 + o(1).$

A comparison of (3) and (2) shows that we have yet to prove two
things: first that $C_2 = 1/2 \log(2\pi)$, and second that the error term ϵ_n,
which we have written merely $o(1)$, really satisfies Eq. (1).

There are many proofs in circulation that the constant in Stirling's
theorem is $\sqrt{2\pi}$, but they are all rather long. In Chap. 9 we shall give
an application of Stirling's theorem in which it will be obvious from
probability considerations that this must be the case. So, for the
present, let us write

$$C_2 = 1/2 \log(2\pi),$$

with the understanding that this will be proved in Chap. 9.

As for the error term, we proceed as follows: Let

$$\alpha_n = \epsilon_n - \frac{1}{12n};$$

$$\beta_n = \epsilon_n - \frac{1}{12n + 6}.$$

Now, (1) reads

(4) $$\alpha_n < 0 < \beta_n.$$

To show these inequalities, we note that (3) tells us that $\epsilon_n \to 0$; therefore $\alpha_n \to 0$ and $\beta_n \to 0$, and (4) follows provided that α_n is steadily increasing and β_n is steadily decreasing. So we shall complete the proof by showing that

(5) $$\alpha_{n+1} - \alpha_n > 0$$

and

(6) $$\beta_{n+1} - \beta_n < 0.$$

First, let us look at

$$\epsilon_{n+1} - \epsilon_n = \log \left[\frac{\dfrac{(n+1)!}{(n+1)^{n+3/2} e^{-n-1} \sqrt{2\pi}}}{\dfrac{n!}{n^{n+1/2} e^{-n} \sqrt{2\pi}}} \right]$$

$$= \log \left[e \left(\frac{n}{n+1} \right)^{n+1/2} \right]$$

$$= 1 + \left(n + \frac{1}{2} \right) \log \left(\frac{n}{n+1} \right).$$

If we set $z = n + \frac{1}{2}$, we have

$$\epsilon_{n+1} - \epsilon_n = 1 + z \log \left(\frac{z - \frac{1}{2}}{z + \frac{1}{2}} \right)$$

$$= 1 + z \log \left[\frac{1 - (1/2z)}{1 + (1/2z)} \right]$$

$$= 1 + z \left[\log \left(1 - \frac{1}{2z} \right) - \log \left(1 + \frac{1}{2z} \right) \right]$$

$$= 1 + z \left[\left(-\frac{1}{2z} - \frac{1}{8z^2} - \frac{1}{24z^3} - \cdots \right) \right.$$
$$\left. - \left(\frac{1}{2z} - \frac{1}{8z^2} + \frac{1}{24z^3} - \cdots \right) \right]$$

$$= 1 + z \left(-\frac{1}{z} - \frac{1}{12z^3} - \frac{1}{80z^5} - \cdots \right)$$

$$= -\frac{1}{12z^2} - \frac{1}{80z^4} - \cdots$$

$$= -\sum_{k=1}^{\infty} \frac{1}{(2k+1)(2z)^{2k}}.$$

Now,

$$\alpha_{n+1} - \alpha_n = \epsilon_{n+1} - \epsilon_n - \frac{1}{12(n+1)} + \frac{1}{12n}$$

$$= \epsilon_{n+1} - \epsilon_n + \frac{1}{12n(n+1)}$$

$$= \epsilon_{n+1} - \epsilon_n + \frac{1}{12(z - \frac{1}{2})(z + \frac{1}{2})}$$

$$= \epsilon_{n+1} - \epsilon_n + \frac{1}{12z^2} \cdot \frac{1}{1 - (1/4z^2)}$$

$$= -\sum_{k=1}^{\infty} \frac{1}{(2k+1)(2z)^{2k}} + \frac{1}{12z^2} \sum_{k=0}^{\infty} \frac{1}{(4z^2)^k}$$

$$= -\sum_{k=1}^{\infty} \frac{1}{(2k+1)(2z)^{2k}} + \sum_{k=1}^{\infty} \frac{1}{3(2z)^{2k}}$$

$$= \sum_{k=1}^{\infty} \frac{2k-2}{3(2k+1)(2z)^{2k}}$$

$$> 0.$$

This proves (5). Equation (6) is much easier:

$$\beta_{n+1} - \beta_n = \epsilon_{n+1} - \epsilon_n - \frac{1}{12(n + \frac{3}{2})} + \frac{1}{12(n + \frac{1}{2})}$$

$$= \epsilon_{n+1} - \epsilon_n - \frac{1}{12(z+1)} + \frac{1}{12z}$$

$$= \epsilon_{n+1} - \epsilon_n + \frac{1}{12z(z+1)}$$

$$< -\frac{1}{12z^2} + \frac{1}{12z(z+1)}$$

$$< 0.$$

This completes the proof of Stirling's theorem.

54. Complex Exponentials

The function e^{iy}, where i is the imaginary unit ($i^2 = -1$), is defined by the series

(1)
$$e^{iy} = 1 + iy + \frac{(iy)^2}{2!} + \frac{(iy)^3}{3!} + \cdots$$

$$= 1 + iy - \frac{y^2}{2!} - \frac{iy^3}{3!} + \cdots .$$

There are a number of properties of this function that we want to list here for use later. If we take the familiar Maclaurin expansions

$$\cos y = 1 - \frac{y^2}{2!} + \frac{y^4}{4!} - \cdots ,$$

$$\sin y = y - \frac{y^3}{3!} + \frac{y^5}{5!} - \cdots ,$$

multiply the second one by i, add and compare (1), we have the Euler formula:

(2) $$e^{iy} = \cos y + i \sin y.$$

Replacing y by $-y$ in (2), we have

$$e^{-iy} = \cos(-y) + i \sin(-y)$$
$$= \cos y - i \sin y;$$

and, subtracting this result from (2), we have

(3) $$\sin y = \frac{1}{2i} (e^{iy} - e^{-iy}).$$

If we plot the complex number e^{iy} in the complex plane, (2) tells us that its coordinates are $\cos y$ and $\sin y$. Hence, its absolute value (distance from the origin) is

$$(\cos^2 y + \sin^2 y)^{\frac{1}{2}} = 1.$$

So we have the important fact that

(4) $$|e^{iy}| = 1$$

for all real y's. In particular, this tells us that the exponential of a pure imaginary is uniformly bounded.

Another important consequence of (2) is the periodicity of e^{iy}. Since

$$\cos(y + 2k\pi) = \cos y$$

and

$$\sin(y + 2k\pi) = \sin y,$$

it follows that

(5) $$e^{i(y+2k\pi)} = e^{iy}$$

for every integer k. From this we obtain the interesting information that, for k an integer,

(6) $$\int_{-\pi}^{\pi} e^{iky} \, dy = \begin{cases} 0 & \text{if } k \neq 0, \\ 2\pi & \text{if } k = 0. \end{cases}$$

To prove this, we note that, if $k = 0$, $e^{iky} = 1$ and

$$\int_{-\pi}^{\pi} dy = 2\pi.$$

If $k \neq 0$,

$$\int_{-\pi}^{\pi} e^{iky} \, dy = \frac{1}{ik} \, e^{iky} \Big|_{-\pi}^{\pi}$$

$$= \frac{1}{ik} \left(e^{ik\pi} - e^{-ik\pi} \right)$$

$$= \frac{1}{ik} \left[e^{ik\pi} - e^{i(k\pi - 2k\pi)} \right]$$

$$= 0$$

because of (5).

55. The Integral of sin x/x

In Chap. 9 we shall want to use the result

(1) $$\int_{-\infty}^{\infty} \frac{\sin x}{x} \, dx = \pi.$$

This result can be found in any good set of tables of definite integrals, but the student might be interested in the following formal development: If we integrate by parts twice, each time differentiating the exponential factor and integrating the trigonometric factor, we have

$$\int_{0}^{\infty} e^{-tx} \cos ux \, dx = \frac{t}{u^2} - \frac{t^2}{u^2} \int_{0}^{\infty} e^{-tx} \cos ux \, dx;$$

and, on solving this equation for the integral, we get

$$\int_{0}^{\infty} e^{-tx} \cos ux \, dx = \frac{t}{u^2 + t^2}.$$

Now, we integrate with respect to u from 0 to 1 and reverse the order of integration on the left-hand side of the equation. This gives us

$$\int_{0}^{\infty} e^{-tx} \frac{\sin x}{x} \, dx = \arctan \frac{1}{t}.$$

Taking the limit under the integral sign can be justified in this case; so we let $t \to 0$ and have

$$\int_{0}^{\infty} \frac{\sin x}{x} \, dx = \frac{\pi}{2}.$$

Now,

$$\frac{\sin(-x)}{-x} = \frac{\sin x}{x};$$

so

$$\int_{-\infty}^{\infty} \frac{\sin x}{x} \, dx = 2 \int_0^{\infty} \frac{\sin x}{x} \, dx = \pi.$$

REFERENCES FOR FURTHER STUDY

Churchill, *Introduction to Complex Variables and Applications*, New York (1948), Chap. 3.

Titchmarsh, *The Theory of Functions*, Oxford (1939), pp. 55–58.

de la Vallée Poussin, *Cours d'analyse infinitésimale*, 1st American ed., New York (1946), Vol. II, Chap. III.

Widder, *Advanced Calculus*, New York (1947), Chap. XI.

PROBLEMS

1. Compute the Stirling theorem approximation to 1!. *Ans.* .92.

2. Compute the Stirling theorem approximation to $n!$ for $n = 1$, $2, \ldots, 10$. Compare the results with the actual values of $n!$. Note that the error itself gets larger as n increases, but the relative error gets smaller. This is typical of asymptotic formulas.

3. Use Stirling's theorem to get a numerical answer to Prob. 1, Chap. 3. Hint: Use logarithms. *Ans.* 4.474×10^{-28}.

4. Use Stirling's theorem to get a numerical answer to Prob. 27, Chap. 4. *Ans.* 2.52×10^{-11}.

5. Using (5), Sec. 51, and (1), Sec. 52, convert (3), Sec. 53, into the form

$$\log \Gamma(n) = (n - \tfrac{1}{2}) \log n - n + C_2 + o(1).$$

Note that this has been proved only for n an integer.

6. It can be shown (cf. Titchmarsh, *The Theory of Functions*, page 58) that

$$\frac{\Gamma(x)}{\Gamma(x + a)} \sim x^{-a}.$$

Use this result in conjunction with Prob. 5 to show that

$$\log \Gamma(x) = (x - \tfrac{1}{2}) \log x - x + C_2 + o(1).$$

Hint: If x is not an integer, set $x = n + a$ where $0 < a < 1$, and apply the formula given above. Simplify by means of (1), Sec. 52.

7. Substitute the result of Prob. 6 into the Legendre formula (11), Sec. 51. Show that all terms except the constants cancel, and obtain the result (not yet proved in the text) that $C_2 = \tfrac{1}{2} \log(2\pi)$.

8. Show that Probs. 5 to 7, in addition to evaluating the constant, give a Stirling approximation to the Γ function:

$$\Gamma(x) \sim x^{x-\frac{1}{2}}e^{-x}\sqrt{2\pi},$$

where x need not be restricted to integer values.

9. Apply (1), Sec. 52, to the formula of Theorem I to get an alternate form of Stirling's theorem:

$$n! = (n + \tfrac{1}{2})^{n+\frac{1}{2}}e^{-n-\frac{1}{2}}\sqrt{2\pi}e^{\eta_n}.$$

10. By the methods used to prove (1), Sec. 53, show that η_n of Prob. 9 satisfies the inequalities

$$-\frac{1}{24n + 12} < \eta_n < -\frac{1}{24n + 13}.$$

11. Apply (9), Sec. 51, to show that

$$\mathrm{B}(n - k, k + 1) = \frac{1}{(n - k)^n\, C_k}.$$

12. Use the result of Prob. 11 to complete Probs. 26 and 27, Chap. I. Hint: The additive constant can be obtained by substituting a specific value of x. Let $x = 1$.

13. The χ^2 distribution with n degrees of freedom is defined by the density function

$$k_n(x) = \frac{1}{2^{n/2}\Gamma(n/2)}\, x^{(n/2)-1}e^{-x/2}$$

for $x > 0$ with $k_n = 0$ for $x \leq 0$. Set up the convolution for k_m and k_n.

Ans. $k_m(u) * k_n(u) = \dfrac{e^{-u/2}}{2^{(m+n)/2}\Gamma(m/2)\Gamma(n/2)} \displaystyle\int_0^u (u - x)^{(m/2)-1}x^{(n/2)-1}\,dx.$

14. Substitute $z = x/u$ in this integral and apply (9), Sec. 51, to show that $k_m * k_n = k_{m+n}$.

15. Starting with Prob. 21, Chap. 5, use Prob. 14 above to give an inductive proof that, if $x_1, x_2, \ldots, x_n$ are independent and each is normally distributed with $\sigma = 1$, then the variable

$$\chi^2 = \sum_{i=1}^{n} x_i^2$$

has a χ^2 distribution with n degrees of freedom.

16. Use (6), Sec. 51, to compute directly $E(\chi^2)$ and $\mathrm{var}(\chi^2)$.

Ans. *n, 2n.*

17. The density function
$$f(x) = \frac{x^{n-1}(1-x)^{m-1}}{\mathrm{B}(n,m)}$$

defines the beta distribution with parameters n and m. Given that x has this distribution, find $E(x)$ and var(x).

Ans. $n/(n+m)$, $nm/(n+m)^2(n+m+1)$.

18. Show from the definition of $o(\ )$ that

$$n \cdot o(1) = o(n),$$
$$o(1)/n = o(1/n),$$
$$[o(1/n)]^2 = o(n^{-2}),$$
$$[O(1/n) + o(1/n)]^2 = O(n^{-2}) = o(1/n).$$

19. Show that if $f(x)$ has a continuous derivative in some neighborhood of 0 and if $f(0) = f'(0) = 0$, then $f(x) = o(x)$ as $x \to 0$. In particular, under these conditions $f(a/n) = o(1/n)$ as $n \to \infty$. Hint: Use Lhopital's rule—$\lim f/g = \lim f'/g'$.

20. Generalize Prob. 19. If $f(x)$ has a continuous nth derivative in some neighborhood of 0 and if

$$f(0) = f'(0) = f''(0) = \cdots = f^{(n)}(0) = 0,$$

then $f(x) = o(x^n)$ as $x \to 0$.

21. Show that, if $f(x)$ has a continuous nth derivative in some neighborhood of 0, then

$$f(x) = f(0) + f'(0)x + \frac{f''(0)}{2!}x^2 + \cdots + \frac{f^{(n)}(0)}{n!}x^n + o(x^n).$$

Hint: Transpose, and apply Prob. 20.

22. Compare the result of Prob. 21 with the Maclaurin formula with remainder:

$$f(x) = f(0) + f'(0)x + \cdots + \frac{f^{(n)}(0)}{n!}x^n + \frac{f^{(n+1)}(\theta x)}{(n+1)!}x^{n+1}.$$

Note that this latter result requires the existence of one more derivative but gives the stronger result, remainder $= O(x^{n+1})$.

23. Show from (1), Sec. 52, that $\lim\limits_{n \to \infty}[1 + (a/n)]^n = e^a$.

24. Show that $n \log[1 + (a/n) + o(1/n)] = a + o(1)$. Hint: Let $z = (a/n) + o(1/n)$, and apply Prob. 21 to $\log(1 + z)$.

25. Show from Prob. 24 that $\lim\limits_{n \to \infty}[1 + (a/n) + o(1/n)]^n = e^a$.

26. From Probs. 21 and 25 show that, if $f(0) = 1$ and $f'(x)$ is continuous in some neighborhood of 0 with $f'(0) = a$, then, for each fixed x, $\lim\limits_{n \to \infty}[f(x/n)]^n = e^{ax}$.

27. Show that $\cos y = \frac{1}{2}(e^{iy} + e^{-iy})$.

28. Show that

$$\sin my \sin ny = -\frac{1}{4}[e^{i(m+n)y} + e^{-i(m+n)y} - e^{i(m-n)y} - e^{i(n-m)y}].$$

29. Using Prob. 28 and (6), Sec. 54, verify that, if m and n are unequal integers,

$$\int_{-\pi}^{\pi} \sin my \sin ny \, dy = 0.$$

30. Show that

$$\int_{-a}^{a} e^{itx} \, dx = \frac{2}{t} \sin at.$$

CHAPTER 8

LIMIT THEOREMS

One of the most important accomplishments of the mathematicians who have worked with probability theory has been the formulation and proof of the so-called limit theorems. An exhaustive study of this body of work is beyond the scope of an elementary course, but we shall do the best we can without resorting to advanced analytical concepts.

Probability limit theorems are concerned with infinite sequences of stochastic variables, and in general they take the form, "If the variables of a sequence satisfy certain conditions, then such and such a law (or formula) applies to that sequence." A given law by itself does not constitute a theorem, but it describes a class of limit theorems—those which state conditions under which the given law holds. The purpose of this chapter is to give a classification of the limit theorems by describing the more important laws that have been studied. Then Chaps. 9, 10, and 11 take up three of these classifications for a more detailed study.

56. The Central Limit Law

Let x_1, x_2, x_3, . . . be an infinite sequence of stochastic variables, and suppose that for each n there is a joint density function for the variables x_1, x_2, . . . , x_n. This joint density function determines a density function for the variable

$$X_n = \sum_{i=1}^{n} (x_i - \bar{x}_i).$$

The question then arises as to the limiting form (as $n \to \infty$) of the density function for X_n. Now (Theorem V, Chap. 6), if the x's are independent,

$$\text{var}(X_n) = \sum_{i=1}^{n} \text{var}(x_i);$$

therefore in all the interesting cases the values of X_n will be too widely dispersed to make the study of X_n itself very profitable. However, the variable

$$S_n = \frac{X_n}{\sqrt{\operatorname{var}(X_n)}}$$

has a variance equal to unity, and the limit of its density function should give us a very good picture of the limiting distribution for the sum of the x's.

The variable S_n is sometimes called the sum in standard units. A deviation of one unit in S_n corresponds to a deviation of σ (one standard deviation) in X_n.

The density function for S_n itself certainly varies from one sequence $\{x_i\}$ to another, and at first one might suspect that the limiting density function would too. It turns out, however, that, for all sequences of x's satisfying a certain rather general condition, the limiting distribution for S_n is the normal distribution. This suggests the first of our important laws.

Definition 1. The sequence x_1, x_2, x_3, . . . of stochastic variables obeys the central limit law provided that, for every a, b with $a \leq b$,

$$\lim_{n \to \infty} pr\{a \leq S_n \leq b\} = \int_a^b \frac{1}{\sqrt{2\pi}} e^{-z^2/2} \, dz,$$

where

$$S_n = \frac{\sum_{i=1}^{n} (x_i - \bar{x}_i)}{\left[\operatorname{var} \left(\sum_{i=1}^{n} x_i \right) \right]^{1/2}}.$$

The history of this important law dates back to the first of the eighteenth century. Apparently de Moivre (1667–1754) was the first to discover that the variables describing a Bernoullian sequence of trials obey the central limit law—though, naturally, he did not state his result in those terms. Laplace (1749–1827) spent some 20 years on the general problem of the limiting distribution of S_n. He made some improvements on de Moivre's proof for the Bernoullian case and was the first to suggest the general theorem that the normal distribution is the limiting one in a wide variety of cases. Laplace gave a proof of this general theorem, but it is not considered satisfactory by present-day standards of rigor. The first really satisfactory proof of Laplace's theorem was given in 1901 by Liapounoff. For this reason, the so-called central limit theorem is frequently referred to as the Laplace-

Liapounoff theorem.   The title "central limit theorem" seems to have been originated by Polya in 1920.   There have been numerous studies of the problem made since 1901.   One important goal of these has been to improve on Liapounoff's description of the class of sequences $\{x_i\}$ for which the law holds.   A significant improvement of this sort was given in 1922 by Lindeberg.   The true importance of Lindeberg's condition appeared in 1935, when Feller showed that it is necessary and sufficient for the law to hold in case the variables x_i are totally independent.   As yet, the theory for dependent variables is very sketchy. Only a few special cases of this type have been treated.

A physical interpretation of the central limit law would be something like this: If a physical effect is due to a large number of independent causes, then regardless of the distributions of the measurements of the individual causes, if the central limit law applies, we should expect the measurements of the over-all effect to exhibit a nearly normal distribution.   Chapter 9 is devoted to a discussion of the conditions under which the central limit law holds, together with a number of applications.

57. The Poisson Distribution

In a central limit law situation the limiting distribution is a continuous one whether the individual stochastic variables are or not. The Poisson law furnishes an example of a discrete limiting distribution.

Definition 2.   A sequence x_1, x_2, x_3, . . . of stochastic variables having probability functions f_1, f_2, f_3, . . . , respectively, obeys the Poisson limit law provided that, for each integer $r > 0$,

$$\lim_{n \to \infty} f_n(r) = \frac{a^r e^{-a}}{r!}.$$

From a theoretical point of view, the Poisson law seems to apply to a much narrower field than the central limit law.   However, the number of practical problems that come within its scope gives it a place of real importance among the limit theorems.   One explanation of this wide applicability lies in the fact that the probability functions

$$(1) \qquad f_n(r) = {}^nC_r \left(\frac{a}{n}\right)^r \left(1 - \frac{a}{n}\right)^{n-r}$$

describe variables obeying the Poisson limit law.   Now, $f_n(r)$, as defined above, is just the probability of r successes in n Bernoullian trials with probability a/n of success on each trial.   If we use the Poisson law to get an approximation for large n and note that n large makes $p = a/n$ small, then we have the usual Poisson theorem for rare events: If p is very small, then the probability of r successes in a large number n of Bernoullian trials is approximately $(np)^r e^{-np}/r!$.

In Chap. 10 we shall give a proof that the Poisson law applies to the case (1), and that proof will include an estimate of the proper interpretation of the words "small," "large," and "approximately" in the above statement. We shall also discuss some specific applications there.

At this stage we should get clearly in mind the distinction between the Poisson limit theorem and the central limit theorem as applied to the case of Bernoullian trials. The number of successes in n Bernoullian trials is the sum of n independent stochastic variables, and it is easy to show that these obey the central limit law. Therefore, the normal density function ought to give us approximate information on probabilities for the number of successes. Where, then, does the Poisson formula come in? The answer is that, if p is very small, it gives a better approximation than the central limit law does.

As approximations to Bernoullian probabilities, then, these two laws cover different cases of the same type of situation. Incorporated in limit theorems, however, they refer to essentially different types of situations. Given a single infinite Bernoullian sequence, p is constant, and the limiting distribution is normal in all cases. However, given a sequence of approximate descriptions of a physical situation each of which consists of a finite set of Bernoullian trials with p changing from one set of trials to another so that np is constant, then the limiting distribution is given by the Poisson formula.

58. The Laws of Large Numbers

Returning now to a sequence $x_1, x_2, x_3, \ldots$ of variables and its partial sums

$$X_n = \sum_{i=1}^{n} (x_i - \bar{x}_i),$$

we define the arithmetic means

$$M_n = \frac{X_n}{n}.$$

It is these variables M_n that the laws of large numbers deal with.

Definition 3. A sequence $x_1, x_2, x_3, \ldots$ of stochastic variables obeys the weak law of large numbers provided that, for every constant $\epsilon > 0$,

$$\lim_{n \to \infty} pr\{|M_n| < \epsilon\} = 1.$$

The weak law of large numbers applies to a very wide variety of situations; and where it does apply, it gives some very interesting information about expectations of stochastic variables. Note that

$$M_n = \frac{1}{n} \sum_{i=n}^{n} x_i - \frac{1}{n} \sum_{i=1}^{n} \bar{x}_i;$$

that is, M_n is the difference between the arithmetic mean of the values of the x_i's and the arithmetic mean of their expectations. The weak law of large numbers might, therefore, be restated in this way: Given any two numbers $\epsilon > 0$ and $\eta > 0$, there is an integer $N = N(\epsilon, \eta)$ such that, if $n > N$, then the probability is greater than $1 - \eta$ that the arithmetic mean of the first n variables will differ from the arithmetic mean of the first n expectations by an amount less in absolute value than ϵ.

From a strictly theoretical point of view, the weak law of large numbers is a first cousin to the central limit law. They are each concerned with the limiting distribution of a normalized sum of n variables from a given sequence. The central limit law states that the limiting distribution for the variable S_n is the normal distribution. The weak law of large numbers states that the limiting distribution for the variables M_n is the so-called unitary distribution—probability of 0 equal to unity, and probability of all other values equal to zero.

In discussing the kinship of the central limit law and the weak law of large numbers, we should point out that the central limit law is the more potent of the two. By this we do not mean that the central limit law always implies the weak law of large numbers (see Probs. 14 and 15 at the end of this chapter); but when they both hold, the central limit law gives far more information. The statement that a sequence of distributions tends to the unitary merely says that with increasing probability the values of the variables cluster about zero, but it says nothing about how the cluster is distributed. For example, each of the following density functions describes a near unitary distribution:

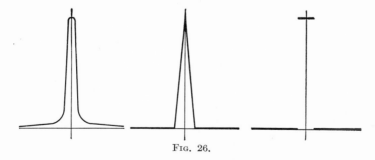

FIG. 26.

However, only the first of these shows promise of being anything like normal after the change of scale $S_n = nM_n/[\mathrm{var}(X_n)]^{1/2}$.

To be more specific, it is easy to show that Bernoullian sequences obey both laws. Therefore, if we toss a coin a large number of times, the weak law of large numbers tells us that there is a probability close to 1 that the number of heads divided by the total number of tosses will be near $\frac{1}{2}$. In terms of distributions, this means that in a large number of sequences of tosses we should expect most of the values of r/n to be near $\frac{1}{2}$. However, for information as to the expected frequency distribution of these values of r/n, we must turn to the central limit law.

While these comments fit the weak law of large numbers into its proper niche in an outline of the theoretical content of the limit theorems, there is another way of looking at it that accomplishes two important ends: (1) gives a picture of the practical interpretation of the law, and (2) suggests the background for a generalization to the so-called strong law of large numbers.

The n variables $x_1, x_2, \ldots, x_n$ define an n-dimensional event space in which each point is represented by a sequence of n numbers (its coordinates), each of which is a possible value of one of the variables x_i. Now, the inequality $|M_n| < \epsilon$ defines a point set $A_{n,\epsilon}$ in this n-dimensional space—the set of all sequences whose arithmetic means differ from the number

$$\frac{1}{n} \sum_{i=1}^{n} \bar{x}_i$$

by an amount less in absolute value than ϵ. The point set $A_{n,\epsilon}$ has a certain probability determined by the joint density (or probability) function for the n-dimensional space. The weak law of large numbers says that for every $\eta > 0$, if we look at the set $A_{n,\epsilon}$ in a space of a sufficiently large number of dimensions, we shall find its probability to be greater than $1 - \eta$.

Suppose the variables x_i represent the results of experiments. The n-dimensional space mentioned above represents the set of all possible sequences of results of the first n experiments. The set $A_{n,\epsilon}$ represents all those sequences of results which satisfy the condition $|M_n| < \epsilon$. If the weak law of large numbers holds, it tells us that, if n is large enough, the sequences of results of the $A_{n,\epsilon}$ type will form a large proportion of the set of all possible sequences of results.

The picture of an event space composed of sequences of numbers suggests the necessary background for a description of the strong law of large numbers. Suppose we consider an event space whose points are *infinite* sequences of numbers. In particular, we want to consider the space of all such sequences $\alpha_1, \alpha_2, \alpha_3, \ldots$, where, for each i, α_i is a possible value of the stochastic variable x_i. The details need not concern us here, but it is possible to define a probability distribution in this space of infinite sequences in terms of the joint distributions for the corresponding spaces of finite sequences. If this is done, then a set of infinite sequences will have a probability. The strong law of large numbers is concerned with the set of infinite sequences $\{\alpha_i\}$ for which

$$\lim \frac{1}{n} \sum_{i=1}^{n} (\alpha_i - \bar{x}_i) = 0.$$

Definition 4. The sequence $x_1, x_2, x_3, \ldots$ of stochastic variables obeys the strong law of large numbers provided that

$$pr\{\lim_{n \to \infty} M_n = 0\} = 1,$$

where

$$M_n = \frac{1}{n} \sum_{i=1}^{n} (x_i - \bar{x}_i).$$

The first thing we should observe about the strong law of large numbers is that it says $M_n \to 0$ with probability 1, not $M_n \to 0$, period. The student is already familiar with the fact that probability 1 does not necessarily mean logical certainty, and (except for certain trivial cases) probability 1 in the strong law of large numbers definitely does not mean certainty. Suppose (as is usually the case) there is some fixed number $\delta > 0$ such that each of the variables x_i can assume a value greater than $\bar{x}_i + \delta$. Then, it is logically possible that every x_i assumes such a value, in which case $M_n > \delta$ for each n, and $\lim M_n \geq \delta$. For example, it is theoretically possible that we get heads on every toss of a coin; therefore it is not logically certain that the ratio of heads to total tosses will tend to $\frac{1}{2}$, though the strong law of large numbers tells us that the probability of this latter event is unity.

In a discrete event space this phenomenon of probability zero for a logically possible event does not occur; so in the strong law of large numbers we must be dealing with a continuous event space. This is, indeed, the case; but the student must not jump to the conclusion that we are restricted to continuous variables for the x_i's.

The example of coin tossing points this out very effectively. A sequence of tosses of a coin may be represented by a sequence of 0's and 1's with the conditions that the jth and kth places in the sequence are independent if $j \neq k$ and for each place the probability of 0 is $\frac{1}{2}$ and so is that of 1. Now, an infinite sequence of 0's and 1's can be thought of as the dyadic expansion of a number between 0 and 1. A dyadic expansion is an expansion in powers of $\frac{1}{2}$ in contrast to a decimal expansion, which is an expansion in powers of $\frac{1}{10}$. For example, in the decimal system

$$.1047 = \frac{1}{10} + \frac{0}{10^2} + \frac{4}{10^3} + \frac{7}{10^4};$$

in the dyadic system

$$.1011 = \frac{1}{2} + \frac{0}{2^2} + \frac{1}{2^3} + \frac{1}{2^4}.$$

Clearly, a dyadic expansion involves only zeros and ones. The dyadic .02 would mean (if anything) .10, just as the decimal .0(10) would mean .10.

So let us think of our infinite sequences of heads and tails as dyadic expansions of numbers between 0 and 1. In this simple case, the mysterious "space of infinite sequences" involved in the strong law of large numbers can be represented as merely the unit interval. Not only this, but the probability distribution is a familiar one. If a point is chosen at random in the unit interval, the probability that the kth place in its dyadic expansion will be 0 is exactly $\frac{1}{2}$; and the jth and kth places are independent for $j \neq k$. (See Prob. 33, Chap. 3, where the analogous property of decimal expansions is pointed out.) So the event space of infinite sequences of coin tosses is represented by the unit interval with a constant density function. Here each variable x_i assumes only two values, but the space of infinite sequences is a familiar example of a continuous event space.

For the purpose of contrasting the weak and strong laws of large numbers, let us assume that our sequence space can be represented by the unit interval with constant density function. We need not stick to dyadic expansions, though. The general picture is that we have stochastic variables M_n—that is, functions $M_n(t)$ defined over the event space $0 \leq t \leq 1$. The connection between this and our original description of the limit laws is that $M_n(t)$ is the average deviation from the mean of the first n values in the particular sequence represented by the point t. For this model the weak law says that for each fixed $\epsilon > 0$ the t set for which $|M_n(t)| \geq \epsilon$ has probability tending to zero. The strong law says that the t set for which $M_n(t) \to 0$ has probability 1.

The thing to note about the weak law is that the t set whose probability is tending to zero may move around in such a way that $M_n(t)$ does not tend to zero for any fixed t. Suppose

$$M_n(t) = \begin{cases} 1 & \text{for } t \text{ in } E_n \\ 0 & \text{otherwise} \end{cases}$$

where E_n is an interval of length $1/n$ with the E_n's laid out end to end and lapping back when they reach the end of the interval:

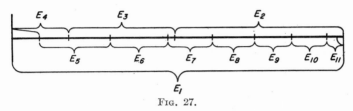

FIG. 27.

In this case,

$$pr\{M_n(t) \neq 0\} \leq \frac{1}{n} \to 0.$$

However, $\Sigma 1/n$ is a divergent series; so these intervals continue to lap back and forth indefinitely so that for no t does $M_n(t)$ become *and remain* close to 0. Thus,

$$pr\{M_n(t) \to 0\} = 0.$$

So the weak law holds, but the strong law does not.

On the other hand, the strong law implies the weak law. Referring again to the unit interval model, let $\epsilon > 0$ be given, and let $B_{k,\epsilon}$ be the set of points t such that $|M_n(t)| < \epsilon$ for $n \geq k$ but not for $n = k - 1$. Now, $M_n(t) \to 0$ means that t must be in a $B_{k,\epsilon}$ set for some k; so if the strong law holds,

$$pr\left\{ \sum_{k=1}^{\infty} B_{k,\epsilon} \right\} = 1.$$

However, we have defined the $B_{k,\epsilon}$'s so that they are disjoint; thus, according to the addition principle,

$$\sum_{k=1}^{\infty} pr\{B_{k,\epsilon}\} = 1.$$

Therefore,

$$\lim_{m \to \infty} pr\left\{ \sum_{k=1}^{m} B_{k,\epsilon} \right\} = \lim_{m \to \infty} \sum_{k=1}^{m} pr\{B_{k,\epsilon}\} = 1.$$

Now, if t is in the set

$$\sum_{k=1}^{m} B_{k,\epsilon},$$

it follows from the definition of the B's that $|M_m(t)| < \epsilon$; so the result above tells us that

$$\lim_{m \to \infty} pr\{|M_m(t)| < \epsilon\} = 1,$$

and this is the weak law.

We suggested that the student follow the above proof with the unit interval model in mind with the idea that that might help him to get a picture of what was going on. We should remark in conclusion, however, that this proof can be completely divorced from the specific model to constitute an argument that the strong law of large numbers always implies the weak law.

59. The Law of the Iterated Logarithm

If a sequence of variables obeys the strong law of large numbers, then, with probability 1, $X_n = o(n)$. The question then arises as to a better estimate of the probable order of magnitude of the sums X_n. It turns out that quite a large number of sequences of stochastic variables satisfy the condition $X_n = O([\mathrm{var}(X_n) \log \log \mathrm{var} \ (X_n)]^{1/2})$ with probability 1 and that for most interesting cases this is the best O relationship that can be obtained with probability 1. Specifically, it has been found that many sequences of stochastic variables obey the following law:

Definition 5. A sequence $x_1,\ x_2,\ x_3,\ \ldots$ of stochastic variables obeys the law of the iterated logarithm provided that the following conditions hold with probability 1: For every $\epsilon > 0$

(1)
$$\frac{|X_n|}{[2 \ \mathrm{var}(X_n) \log \log \mathrm{var}(X_n)]^{1/2}} < 1 + \epsilon$$

for all but a finite number of values of n, and

(2)
$$\frac{|X_n|}{[2 \ \mathrm{var}(X_n) \log \log \mathrm{var}(X_n)]^{1/2}} > 1 - \epsilon$$

for an infinite number of values of n.

We shall not attempt to give any detailed discussion of the law of the iterated logarithm in this book. Theorems giving conditions for the validity of the other limit laws are given in the next three chapters. Since there is no chapter on the iterated logarithm law, we might state here (without proof) the standard theorem:

Theorem I (*Kolmogoroff*). If the stochastic variables x_1, x_2, x_3, . . . are individually bounded by the numbers K_n (that is, $pr\{|x_n| > K_n\} = 0$ for each n) and if

$$K_n = o(\text{var}(X_n)[\log \log \text{var}(X_n)]^{-\frac{1}{2}}),$$

then the sequence $\{x_n\}$ obeys the law of the iterated logarithm.

There is an example, due to Marcinkiewicz and Zygmund, to the effect that if the o in Theorem I is replaced by O, the result no longer holds; but the surprising thing is that in this example it is (2) that fails, not (1) as one might suspect. In other words, if the values of the individual variables x_i are too big, the sums X_n may be too small!

There are many sequences of stochastic variables to which both the central limit law and the law of the iterated logarithm apply, and the contrasting import of these two laws gives a very good picture of the notion of random sequences of numbers. Suppose we consider an infinite sequence of experiments to which both laws apply. The central limit law says that the possible sequences of results are so arranged that, for every sufficiently large n, roughly two-thirds of them satisfy the condition $|S_n| \leq 1$ and roughly 95 per cent of them satisfy the condition $|S_n| \leq 2$. However, the law of the iterated logarithm says that for almost every individual sequence we have

$$|S_n| > (1 - \epsilon)[2 \log \log \text{var}(X_n)]^{\frac{1}{2}}$$

an infinite number of times.

REFERENCES FOR FURTHER STUDY

Feller, "The Fundamental Limit Theorems in Probability," *Bull. Amer. Math. Soc.*, vol. 51, pp. 800–832, 1945.

Halmos, "The Foundations of Probability."

PROBLEMS

1. Show that, for a Bernoullian sequence of trials,

$$M_n = \frac{r}{n} - p,$$

and

$$S_n = \frac{r - np}{\sqrt{npq}}.$$

2. State the weak and strong laws of large numbers for Bernoullian sequences of trials.

Ans.   Weak law: Given $\epsilon > 0$, $pr\left\{\left|\dfrac{r}{n} - p\right| < \epsilon\right\} \to 1$.

Strong law: $pr\left\{\dfrac{r}{n} \to p\right\} = 1$.

3. Find the probability function for S_n in the case of a Bernoullian sequence, and state the central limit law in terms of this probability function.   *Ans.* $\lim\limits_{n \to \infty} \sqrt{npq}\ {}^nC_{np+z\sqrt{npq}}\,p^{np+z\sqrt{npq}}q^{nq-z\sqrt{npq}} = \dfrac{1}{\sqrt{2\pi}}\,e^{-z^2/2}$.

4. Find M_n and S_n for a Poisson sequence of trials (Prob. 12,

Chap. 6).   *Ans.* $M_n = \dfrac{r}{n} - p,\qquad S_n = r - np\bigg/\left(\sum\limits_{i=1}^{n} p_i q_i\right)^{1/2}$.

5. State the central limit law and the weak and strong laws of large numbers for a Poisson sequence of trials.

Ans.   Central limit law: $pr\left\{a \le \dfrac{r - np}{(\Sigma p_i q_i)^{1/2}} \le b\right\} \to \displaystyle\int_a^b \dfrac{1}{\sqrt{2\pi}}\,e^{-z^2/2}\,dz$.

Weak law: Given $\epsilon > 0$, $pr\left\{\left|\dfrac{r}{n} - p\right| < \epsilon\right\} \to 1$.

Strong law: $pr\left\{\dfrac{r}{n} \to p\right\} = 1$.

6. Let each of the variables $x_1, x_2, x_3, \ldots$ have a Poisson distribution (probability function $a^{x_i}e^{-a}/x_i!$), and let them be independent. Setting

$$X_n = \sum_{i=1}^{n} x_i,$$

show that

$$M_n = \frac{X_n}{n} - a,$$

and

$$S_n = \frac{X_n - na}{\sqrt{na}}.$$

7. State the weak and strong laws of large numbers for the sequences of variables in Prob. 6.

Ans.   Weak law: Given $\epsilon > 0$, $pr\left\{\left|\dfrac{X_n}{n} - a\right| < \epsilon\right\} \to 1$.   Strong

law: $pr\left\{\dfrac{X_n}{n} \to a\right\} = 1$.

8. Find the probability function for S_n in Prob. 6, and state the central limit law in terms of this probability function. Hint: See Prob. 17, Chap. 5. *Ans.* $\displaystyle\lim_{n\to\infty} \sqrt{na}\,\frac{(na)^{na+z\sqrt{na}}e^{-na}}{(na+z\sqrt{na})!} = \frac{1}{\sqrt{2\pi}}\,e^{-z^2/2}$.

9. Show that, if x_1, x_2, x_3, ... are independent and each is normally distributed, then the central limit law holds. Hint: See Corollary 1 to Theorem X, Chap. 5.

10. Let x_1, x_2, x_3, ... be independent and each normally distributed with variance unity. Setting

$$\chi^2 = \sum_{i=1}^{n} x_i^2,$$

find M_n and S_n for the sequence $\{x_i^2\}$.

Ans. $\displaystyle M_n = \frac{\chi^2}{n} - 1, \qquad S_n = \frac{\chi^2 - n}{\sqrt{2n}}.$

11. State the strong and weak laws of large numbers for the squares of independent normally distributed variables.

Ans. Weak law: Given $\epsilon > 0$, $\displaystyle pr\left\{\left|\frac{\chi^2}{n} - 1\right| < \epsilon\right\} \to 1$. Strong law: $\displaystyle pr\left\{\frac{\chi^2}{n} \to 1\right\} = 1.$

12. In terms of probabilities for χ^2, state the central limit law for the squares of independent normally distributed variables.

$$\textit{Ans.} \quad pr\left\{a \le \frac{\chi^2 - n}{\sqrt{2n}} \le b\right\} \to \int_a^b \frac{1}{\sqrt{2\pi}}\,e^{-z^2/2}\,dz.$$

13. Find the density function for S_n in Prob. 10, and state the central limit law for the squares of independent normally distributed variables in terms of this density function. Hint: See Prob. 13, Chap. 7.

Ans. $\displaystyle\lim_{n\to\infty} \frac{1}{2^{n/2}\Gamma(n/2)}\,(n + z\sqrt{2n})^{(n/2)-1}\,e^{-(n+z\sqrt{2n})/2} = \frac{1}{\sqrt{2\pi}}\,e^{-z^2/2}.$

14. Let the stochastic variable x_k assume the values $\pm\sqrt{2k-1}$ with probability $\frac{1}{2}$ each. Let the x_k's be independent. Show that in this case $S_n = M_n$; so the central limit law and the law of large numbers cannot both hold. Actually, the central limit law holds, and the law of large numbers does not. (See Prob. 3, Chap. 9.)

15. Show that, if $\mathrm{var}(X_n) = o(n^2)$, then the central limit law implies the weak law of large numbers. Hint: In this case $M_n = S_n \cdot o(1)$, and

$$\int_{-\epsilon/o(1)}^{\epsilon/o(1)} \frac{1}{\sqrt{2\pi}}\,e^{-z^2/2}\,dz \to 1.$$

16. Does the strong law of large numbers state that in a sequence of Bernoullian trials the number of successes minus the expected number will very likely tend to zero?

Ans. No; compare the inequalities $|(r/n) - p| < \epsilon$ and $|r - np| < \epsilon$.

17. Assuming the central limit law to hold for Bernoullian trials, show that, no matter how large the constant K may be,

$$pr\{|r - np| < K\} \to 0.$$

18. Show from Prob. 17 that a gambler with a finite amount of capital who plays a perfectly equitable game has a probability of going broke arbitrarily close to 1 if only he plays long enough.

CHAPTER 9

THE CENTRAL LIMIT THEOREM

As we pointed out in Chap. 8, the most general form of the central limit theorem for independent variables is that given by Lindeberg. We shall begin our discussion by stating the Lindeberg theorem without proof. This should at least satisfy the student's curiosity as to what the best possible condition for the validity of the central limit law looks like. While we have the Lindeberg condition before us, we shall derive from it certain corollaries describing some of the more useful cases of the central limit theorem. The chief virtue of the Lindeberg condition is generality, not simplicity; so the corollaries may well be of more value than the theorem.

Turning to the question of proofs, we want to outline the method of characteristic functions. This was Liapounoff's method of attack, and it remains the favorite tool of the statisticians in dealing with limit theorems generally. While a rigorous development of this method is a little too advanced for an elementary course, the formal work can be carried through; and from this part of our discussion the student should get an intuitive idea as to why the normal distribution appears as the limiting distribution for S_n in such a wide variety of cases. This is, perhaps, the most important part of the chapter, because without these sections the student has nothing but our word for it that the central limit law applies to anything except Bernoullian sequences.

We shall conclude with a detailed discussion of the Bernoullian case. Using essentially the method of de Moivre, we can give a complete proof without getting above the analytical level on which we are trying to pitch this book. It might seem that we include this proof only because we think that there ought to be a proof of something in this chapter; but, actually there are two concrete results of this effort. In this case we are able to give an understandable estimate of the error term, and in the course of our proof we run across a very clear explanation of the need for the Poisson distribution as an alternate approximation formula in case p is small.

60. Notation

In Chap. 8 we saw that the central limit law was concerned with sums of variables of the form $x_k - \bar{x}_k$. To simplify the notation, let us make it a standard practice to consider these translated variables. Their distinguishing characteristic is that each has mean zero, but [see (*b*) of Theorem IV, Chap. 6] variances are not affected by this maneuver. As long as the variables x_k all have expectations, these translations can always be performed; so the hypothesis $\bar{x}_k = 0$, which appears in all our statements of the central limit theorem, is not restrictive, only explanatory.

To avoid repetition, let us explain once and for all the principal symbols to be used throughout this chapter.

x_k: One of a sequence of stochastic variables.   As noted above, we shall always assume $\bar{x}_k = 0$

f_k: The density function for x_k

$$X_n: \quad \sum_{k=1}^{n} x_k$$

b_k: $\operatorname{var}(x_k)$

B_n: $\operatorname{var}(X_n)$

S_n: $X_n/\sqrt{B_n}$

The classical central limit law (Definition 1, Chap. 8) cannot even be formulated unless B_n exists.   Therefore, we shall assume without stopping to say so in each theorem that the second moments of the variables always exist.   It has been found profitable (even in cases where B_n exists) to generalize this definition by dividing the sums X_n by something other than $\sqrt{B_n}$.   However, for an introductory course, we have decided to confine ourselves to the Laplacian form of the central limit law given in Chap. 8.

There is one trivial case of the central limit theorem that we should dispose of before beginning a general discussion.   If all the variables x_k are normally distributed, then by Corollary 1 to Theorem X, Chap. 5, each of the variables S_n has a normal distribution with variance unity; so the central limit law obviously applies.   Having noted this special case, let us now agree to exclude it from consideration in all further discussions.   This will simplify the statement of theorems in several instances.

61. The Lindeberg Version—Informal Discussion

As we pointed out in Chap. 8, Lindeberg gave a very interesting condition for the validity of the central limit law, and Feller proved some time later that this condition is the best possible for the case of independent variables.   We state this result here without proof.

Theorem I (*Lindeberg-Feller*). If the stochastic variables x_k are totally independent and each has mean zero, a necessary and sufficient condition that

$$\lim_{n \to \infty} pr\{a \leq S_n \leq b\} = \frac{1}{\sqrt{2\pi}} \int_a^b e^{-z^2/2} \, dz$$

is that, for every $\epsilon > 0$,

(1) $$\lim_{n \to \infty} \max_{k \leq n} \frac{1}{b_k} \int_{|z| \geq \epsilon \sqrt{B_n}} z^2 f_k(z) dz = 0.$$

There are a number of interesting observations that can be made about the Lindeberg condition (1).

Corollary 1.   If the Lindeberg condition holds, $B_n \to \infty$.

For independent variables, B_n is the sum of the positive quantities b_k and so is monotone-increasing. Therefore, it either tends to ∞ or is bounded. Suppose there were a constant M such that $B_n \leq M$ for all n's. Then, all we have to do is choose ϵ so that

$$\int_{|z| \geq \epsilon \sqrt{M}} z^2 f_1(z) dz > \frac{b_1}{2},$$

and the required maximum will be greater than $\frac{1}{2}$ for all n's. This clearly contradicts (1).

The converse to Corollary 1 is not true. If $B_n \to \infty$, then, for each fixed k, the integral in (1) will tend to zero; but it does not follow that the maximum called for in (1) will tend to zero. We shall see an example of this in the next section.

First, however, let us note some important special cases in which the condition $B_n \to \infty$ is sufficient for the central limit law to hold.

Corollary 2.   If the variables x_k are independent and uniformly bounded (*i.e.*, there is a constant K such that $pr\{|x_k| \geq K\} = 0$ for every k), then the condition $B_n \to \infty$ implies that the sequence $\{x_k\}$ obeys the central limit law.

For each $\epsilon > 0$, $\epsilon \sqrt{B_n} \to \infty$; and as soon as $\epsilon \sqrt{B_n} > K$, the integral in (1) is zero for every k. Therefore, the Lindeberg condition is obviously satisfied.

Corollary 3.   If the variables x_k are independent and identical (*i.e.*, all have the same density function) and have second moments, then the sequence $\{x_k\}$ obeys the central limit law.

Since the variables x_k are identical, the variances b_k are all the same. Let us call them b.   Since the variables x_k are independent, we have by Theorem V, Chap. 6,

$$B_n = nb \to \infty.$$

Therefore, as noted above, the integral in (1) tends to zero for each fixed k.   Now, with the variables identical, the maximum called for in (1) is given by any term we happen to choose—given, say, by $k = 1$ for every n.   So, if the individual integrals tend to zero, the maximum does and the Lindeberg condition is satisfied.

Despite our comment in the previous section that we are automatically assuming that second moments exist, we made special mention of this in Corollary 3 to eliminate possible confusion.   The oldest known example of the failure of the central limit law (discovered by Cauchy) involves identical variables whose second moments do not exist.

62. Examples—Failure of the Law

In any discussion of the central limit law it should be pointed out that, while it applies to a wide variety of cases, it is by no means universally applicable.   In a later section of this chapter we shall describe the more profound example of Cauchy.   Here, we want to give two rather trivial examples in which the Lindeberg condition is not satisfied.   It then follows from Feller's result that at least the classical version of the central limit law fails for these examples.

The easiest way to construct such an example is to note Corollary 1 to Theorem I and take a sequence of variables for which B_n is bounded. Let x_k be defined as follows.

$$\begin{array}{ccc} x_k: & -\tfrac{1}{2}^k & \tfrac{1}{2}^k \\ f_k(x_k): & \tfrac{1}{2} & \tfrac{1}{2} \end{array}$$

Here

$$b_k = \frac{1}{2}\cdot\left(\frac{-1}{2^k}\right)^2 + \frac{1}{2}\cdot\left(\frac{1}{2^k}\right)^2 = \frac{1}{4^k}.$$

If the variables are independent, Theorem V, Chap. 6, applies, and

$$B_n = \sum_{k=1}^{n} \frac{1}{4^k} < \sum_{k=1}^{\infty} \frac{1}{4^k} = \frac{1}{3}.$$

However, we said in the last section that we may have $B_n \to \infty$ and still not have the Lindeberg condition satisfied. An example of this situation is given by the variables x_k defined as follows.

$$x_k: \quad -2^{k+1} \qquad 0 \qquad 2^{k+1}$$
$$f_k(x_k): \quad \tfrac{1}{2}^{k+3} \quad 1 - \tfrac{1}{2}^{k+2} \quad \tfrac{1}{2}^{k+3}$$

Here

$$b_k = \frac{1}{2^{k+3}} \cdot (-2^{k+1})^2 + \frac{1}{2^{k+3}} \cdot (2^{k+1})^2 = 2^k;$$

so

$$B_n = \sum_{k=1}^{n} 2^k = 2^{n+1} - 2.$$

However, the two nonzero values of x_n are both greater in absolute value than B_n, and the second moment of those two values is exactly b_n. So, taking $\epsilon = 1$ in the Lindeberg condition and setting $k = n$ in each case, we see that the required maximum is identically 1

63. Normal Distributions in Nature

There are many examples of physical phenomena for which experimental evidence indicates approximately normal distributions. In biology, many physical measurements on living organisms, tabulated for a large population, exhibit a nearly normal frequency distribution. In physics, the results of a series of attempts at the exact measurement of a quantity are usually very nearly normally distributed. In ballistics, the pattern of hits from a large number of shots fired at a fixed target usually forms something that resembles a normal distribution. In thermodynamics, the distribution of molecular velocities in an ideal gas is very close to normal.

On seeing these and other examples of normal distributions in nature, anyone familiar with the central limit theorem would quite naturally suspect that it had something to do with the situation. The usual interpretation is that such effects are the result of a large number of essentially independent causes and so can be expressed as the sum of a large number of independent stochastic variables, each variable representing the effect due to a single cause. This "hypothesis of elementary causes" is certainly plausible as a *possible* explanation of the occurrence of normal distributions in nature. However, it is hardly justifiable as *the* explanation. There are other hypotheses than those of the central limit theorem that lead to a normal distribution. (See, for instance, Levy and Roth, *Elements of Probability*, pages 118 to 124.)

The hypothesis of elementary causes is an interesting one, and it may well furnish the explanation for many of the observed normal distributions of natural phenomena. However, the most satisfactory applications of the central limit theorem found so far are not those based on this idea. Furthermore, in many cases the most convincing evidence in favor of normal distributions is purely experimental and has nothing to do with the central limit theorem.

Another thing we should bear in mind is that the simple hypothesis that a phenomenon is due to a large number of causes does not necessarily lead to the central limit law. If there is one dominant cause, modified by a number of second-order effects, the distribution of the over-all effect should be essentially that of the major cause—which may not be normal at all. This is readily explained by Corollary 1 to Theorem I. If the second-order effects are definitely just that, B_n remains only a little larger than b_1 and the central limit theorem does not apply.

Finally, then, we might say a word or two about the use of normal distributions in statistics. In the next two sections we shall discuss two examples in which we can pull our way up via the central limit theorem from a sequence of more or less arbitrary distributions to something that is normal or based on the normal distribution. These are only by way of example. There are many other uses for the central limit theorem in statistics. However, there is another body of statistical formulas based on the assumption that the population being studied is normally distributed. (See, for instance, Uspensky, *Introduction to Mathematical Probability*, Chap. XVI.) We can think of two good reasons why any study of statistics involves a lot of work with normal populations. One is that this is the field that has proved most susceptible to investigation, and so there is more known about it. The other is the point we are concerned with in this section, *viz.*, for first one reason and then another there are quite a lot of normal distributions among the things statisticians study.

Statistical theories based on normally distributed populations are not at all out of order as long as we realize that the normal distribution is only something that is frequently encountered, not something guaranteed in all situations by the theory of probability.

64. Example—Sample Means

Let us turn now to some of the things the central limit theorem can actually prove for the statistician. The first thing we should note is that the process of sampling furnishes an example of a sequence of stochastic variables. Suppose there is a population of some sort for which we are interested in a certain measurement connected with the individual members. For example, suppose we are interested in the height of American school children, the income of American families, the butterfat content of milk sold by a certain dairy, the number of defective cartridges per case in those manufactured by a certain company, etc. If we pick a single item (*i.e.*, school child, family, quart of milk, or case of cartridges) at random, there is a probability distribution for the various possible results we may get on measuring this sample item. That is, the result of an individual sample measurement is a stochastic variable. So the usual collection of a number of such sample measurements forms a sequence of stochastic variables.

Let us suppose that each sample measurement is independent of all the others. In sampling from a fixed population, this means random sampling with replacements—a practice not usually followed. We want to use this independence hypothesis here, but this does not completely invalidate our results. The degree of dependence of samples from a very large population is probably so small that it does not introduce appreciable errors. Furthermore, in the examples of sampling from a production line (milk, cartridges, etc.) the hypothesis of independence seems reasonable anyway.

The result of each sample measurement is a stochastic variable with a probability distribution given by the distribution of measurements for the entire population. This distribution is unknown, of course (otherwise there would be no point in sampling); but in general it is bounded and therefore must have a mean $\bar{x}$ and a variance σ^2.

Let $x_1, x_2, \ldots, x_n$ be the results of the first n sample measurements. Each x_k is a stochastic variable with mean $\bar{x}$ and variance σ^2. Therefore,

$$E\left(\sum_{k=1}^{n} x_k\right) = n\bar{x};$$

and since the x_k's are independent,

$$\mathrm{var}\left(\sum_{k=1}^{n} x_k\right) = n\sigma^2.$$

Since these are identical variables (even though their common distribution is completely unknown), Corollary 3 to Theorem I applies, and

$$\lim_{n \to \infty} pr\left\{a \leq \frac{\sum_{k=1}^{n} x_k - n\bar{x}}{\sigma \sqrt{n}} \leq b\right\} = \int_a^b \frac{1}{\sqrt{2\pi}} e^{-z^2/2}\, dz.$$

Now, we let

$$-a = b = \frac{\epsilon \sqrt{n}}{\sigma};$$

and our result reduces to

$$pr \left\{ \left| \frac{1}{n} \sum_{k=1}^{n} x_k - \bar{x} \right| < \epsilon \right\} \simeq \int_{-\epsilon\sqrt{n}/\sigma}^{\epsilon\sqrt{n}/\sigma} \frac{1}{\sqrt{2\pi}} e^{-z^2/2} \, dz,$$

for large n.

The variable $(1/n) \Sigma x_k$—the arithmetic mean of the sample measurements—is called the *sample mean*. We thus have an estimate of the probability that the sample mean differs from the true mean $\bar{x}$ by less than any given amount. Since $\epsilon \sqrt{n}/\sigma \to \infty$ as $n \to \infty$, this probability tends to 1.

This last result would follow more directly from the law of large numbers. The significant contribution of the central limit theorem is that the sample mean is approximately normally distributed with expectation $\bar{x}$ and variance σ^2/n. Furthermore, this is true no matter what the distribution is in the population from which we are sampling. Thus, if we have some information on the size of σ^2, we can find from a table of the normal distribution the probability that the sample mean will differ from the true mean by any given amount.

We shall return to this problem in Chap. 11, where we shall show how the law of large numbers can be used to justify the usual estimate of σ^2 from the sample data. Just now we might note a very simple case in which we can get a lot of information without knowing the actual value of σ^2. Suppose our samples are a Bernoullian sequence of trials. That is, the result of each sample is either yes or no. The sample mean is then r/n, the ratio of the number of yeses to the number of samples. The true mean is p, and so we have

$$pr \left\{ \left| \frac{r}{n} - p \right| < \epsilon \right\} \simeq \int_{-\epsilon\sqrt{n}/\sigma}^{\epsilon\sqrt{n}/\sigma} \frac{1}{\sqrt{2\pi}} e^{-z^2/2} \, dz.$$

Now, in this case $\sigma^2 = pq \leq \frac{1}{4}$; so

$$pr \left\{ \left| \frac{r}{n} - p \right| < \epsilon \right\} \geq \int_{-2\epsilon\sqrt{n}}^{2\epsilon\sqrt{n}} \frac{1}{\sqrt{2\pi}} e^{-z^2/2} \, dz.$$

If we note, for instance, that according to the tables

$$\int_{-2}^{2} \frac{1}{\sqrt{2\pi}} e^{-z^2/2} \, dz \simeq .95,$$

we see that with probability at least .95 we have the experimental ratio within ϵ of the theoretical probability provided that $\epsilon \sqrt{n} \geq 1$. For example, we get an estimate of p correct to within .01 with probability .95 provided that .01 $\sqrt{n} \geq 1$, or $n \geq 10{,}000$. This is taking the maximum value for σ^2. If there is good reason to believe that p is noticeably different from $\frac{1}{2}$, we can improve this estimate.

65. Example—The χ^2 Test

The χ^2 test of significance for sample data is a standard tool in present-day statistical practice. A complete derivation of it is a little over our heads in this course, but we have developed enough of the basic ideas to give the student some conception of what is involved.

The probability distribution of a certain population is assumed to be known. Then samples are taken from this population. Now, we should not expect the frequency distribution of the samples to follow the theoretical distribution exactly, but we want to get some measure of the deviation of the sample distribution from the theoretical one that will give us an idea of the consistency of our theoretical assumption with the experimental results.

If the total range of the sample values is divided into m intervals, the theoretical distribution gives us a probability $p_i(i = 1, 2, \ldots, m)$ that a sample will fall in each of the intervals. So the expected number in the ith interval out of a total of n sample values is np_i. If r_i is the actual number of samples falling in the ith interval, the sum of the squares of the deviations

$$\sum_{i=1}^{m} (r_i - np_i)^2$$

constitutes a reasonable measure of the discrepancy between theoretical and experimental distributions.

It turns out that things work better if we use

$$\chi^2 = \sum_{i=1}^{m} \frac{(r_i - np_i)^2}{np_i}.$$

Now, the problem is to find the probability distribution for χ^2. If we let

$$x_i = \frac{r_i - np_i}{\sqrt{np_i}},$$

we have

$$\chi^2 = \sum_{i=1}^{m} x_1^2.$$

This reminds us of Prob. 15, Chap. 7, in which we had the sum of squares of independent normally distributed variables. Each x_i is just a linear function of r_i, the number of successes in n independent trials with probability p_i of success on each trial; therefore, as $n \to \infty$, the individual x_i's are asymptotically normal. However, they are not independent. If we remember that

$$\sum_{i=1}^{m} p_i = 1 \quad \text{and} \quad \sum_{i=1}^{m} r_i = n,$$

it is easily seen that

$$\sum_{i=1}^{m} x_i \sqrt{p_i} = 0.$$

That is, $m - 1$ of the x_i's determine the other one completely. Furthermore, since this relation is a linear one, it tells us that the x_i's all lie in an $(m - 1)$-dimensional hyperplane; i.e., their joint distribution is $(m - 1)$-dimensional.

As we noted above, the individual x_i's have distributions that tend to the normal. It does not follow that they are asymptotically in normal correlation, but it is not surprising that this is the case. This we shall not attempt to prove. It can be obtained from a multidimensional generalization of the central limit theorem. Now, in Theorem X, Chap. 5, we proved that two variables in normal correlation must be linear combinations of some pair of independent normally distributed variables. This, too, can be generalized to any number of dimensions with the result that in their limiting form the variables x_i, contained in an $(m - 1)$-dimensional space, must be linear combinations of $m - 1$ independent normally distributed variables u_1, u_2, . . . , u_{m-1}.

Again we omit the details, but it turns out that, because of the strategic choice of constants we made in defining the x_i's, each of the variables u_i has variance unity and

$$\sum_{i=1}^{m-1} u_i^2 = \sum_{i=1}^{m} x_i^2 = \chi^2.$$

So, as $n \to \infty$, the distribution of χ^2 tends to that of the sum of squares of $m - 1$ independent normally distributed variables. By Prob. 15, Chap. 7,

$$\lim_{n \to \infty} pr\{\chi^2 \geq \chi_0^2\} = \int_{\chi_0^2}^{\infty} \frac{1}{2^{(m-1)/2}\Gamma[(m - 1)/2]} z^{(m-3)/2} e^{-z/2} \, dz.$$

This χ^2 distribution has been tabulated extensively, and from these tables we can find an approximation to the probability that a set of samples will deviate (in the sense of this test) by more than a given amount from the theoretical frequency.

The student should bear in mind that this is an asymptotic formula, valid only for large n—we shall not attempt to work out an estimate of how large. Suffice it to say that most authorities agree that it should be used only if n is so large that the expected number np_i of samples per interval is at least 10 for every interval. The student should note that this does not require a large number of intervals. As a matter of fact, the fewer intervals there are, the fewer samples it takes to get the expected number per interval up to 10; though, of course, the fewer intervals we use, the less information we get. Finally, we might note that, if the number m of intervals is very large (and the number n of samples sufficiently larger), the formula in this section becomes unwieldy; and we can use the central limit theorem again—this time taking a limit on m. For an outline of this procedure, see Prob. 8 at the end of this chapter.

66. Characteristic Functions

If $f(x)$ is the density function for a stochastic variable x, we define the *characteristic function* for x as

$$(1) \qquad \varphi(t) = \int_{-\infty}^{\infty} e^{itx} f(x)\,dx.$$

In the light of Theorem I, Chap. 6, we can say that $\varphi(t)$ is the expectation of e^{itx}. The characteristic function is the principal tool in the Liapounoff proof of the central limit theorem. That proof will be outlined in the next section. Here we want to indicate as best we can the properties of characteristic functions that will be needed.

First, we might note that every distribution has a characteristic function. The integral defining $\varphi(t)$ has to be absolutely convergent because the integral of $f(x)$ is, and e^{itx} is bounded. The second important thing is this:

Theorem II. The characteristic function uniquely determines the distribution.

As a matter of fact, in all cases (discrete, continuous, and otherwise), the distribution function $F(u) = pr\{x \le u\}$ is given by the formula

$$(2) \qquad F(u) - F(a) = \lim_{T \to \infty} \frac{1}{2\pi} \int_{-T}^{T} \frac{e^{-itu} - e^{ita}}{it} \varphi(t)\,dt$$

whenever u and a are points of continuity of F. A rigorous proof of Theorem II is beyond the scope of this book, but we might make it seem reasonable by going through the formal computations for the special cases with which we are familiar. If there is a density function $f(x)$, it is the derivative at $u = x$ of $F(u)$. Without attempting to justify the procedure, let us take the limit as $T \to \infty$ and the derivative with respect to u both under the integral sign in (2). Then, the substitution $u = x$ gives

$$f(x) = \frac{1}{2\pi} \int_{-\infty}^{\infty} e^{-itx}\varphi(t)dt.$$

By continuing to ignore the finer points that need rigorous justification, we can give a formal indication that this last formula is correct.

$$\int_{-k}^{k} e^{-ity}\varphi(t)dt = \int_{-k}^{k} e^{-ity} \int_{-\infty}^{\infty} e^{itx} f(x)dx \, dt$$

$$= \int_{-\infty}^{\infty} \int_{-k}^{k} e^{it(x-y)} f(x)dt \, dx$$

$$= \int_{-\infty}^{\infty} \left.\frac{e^{it(x-y)}}{i(x-y)}\right|_{-k}^{k} f(x)dx$$

$$= \int_{-\infty}^{\infty} \frac{2 \sin k(x-y)}{x-y} f(x)dx.$$

Letting $w = k(x - y)$, we have

$$\int_{-\infty}^{\infty} e^{-ity}\varphi(t)dt = \lim_{k \to \infty} \int_{-\infty}^{\infty} \frac{2 \sin w}{w} f\left(\frac{w}{k} + y\right) dw.$$

If we can take the limit under the integral sign (a step that is unusually hard to justify in this particular case) and if f is continuous, the application of (1), Sec. 55, gives us

$$\int_{-\infty}^{\infty} e^{-ity}\varphi(t)dt = 2\pi f(y).$$

In the discrete case, the proof is much simpler, but it is not nearly as convincing because the reduction of (2) to a formula for the probability function is not at all obvious intuitively. The best we can do is to state it and indicate the proof. Let us assume that the values of x are all integers. Then the probability function—which we shall now write $f(n)$—is given by the formula

$$f(n) = \frac{1}{2\pi} \int_{-\pi}^{\pi} e^{-int}\varphi(t)dt.$$

To prove this, we note that

$$\varphi(t) = \sum_k e^{ikt} f(k);$$

so, multiplying by e^{-int} and integrating, we have

$$\int_{-\pi}^{\pi} \sum_k e^{i(k-n)t} f(k) dt.$$

If the sum is a finite one, there is no argument; but, even for an infinite series, it is not hard to justify integrating term by term in this case. So we have

$$\sum_k f(k) \int_{-\pi}^{\pi} e^{i(k-n)t} dt = 2\pi f(n)$$

because by (6), Sec. 54, all the integrals vanish except the one for $k = n$, and it is equal to 2π.

We have gone to all this trouble to make Theorem II seem reasonable to the student because, if each characteristic function uniquely determines a distribution, then it is not unreasonable to suspect that the limit of a sequence of characteristic functions would determine a distribution function which is the limit of the corresponding sequence of distribution functions. This is, indeed, the case, but we shall not even try to prove it here. We merely list for reference the following:

Theorem III. If a sequence φ_n of characteristic functions converges to a characteristic function φ, then the corresponding sequence of distribution functions converges to the distribution function determined by φ.

If we accept Theorem III, we are well on the road to proving the central limit theorem. All we have to do is show that the characteristic function for S_n converges to the characteristic function for the normal distribution. Now, S_n is the sum of the first n x's divided by $\sqrt{B_n}$; so we have three more preliminary questions: (1) What does the characteristic function of a sum look like? (2) What happens to the characteristic function when we divide a variable by a constant? (3) What is the characteristic function of the normal distribution?

Theorem IV. If x and y are independent and have characteristic functions φ_1 and φ_2, respectively, then $\varphi_1 \varphi_2$ is the characteristic function for $x + y$.

By Theorem V, Chap. 5, e^{itx} and e^{ity} are independent. Now, $e^{it(x+y)} = e^{itx}e^{ity}$; so the characteristic function for $x + y$ is just the expectation of a product of independent variables, and the result follows from Theorem III, Chap. 6.

Theorem V. If $\varphi(t)$ is the characteristic function for x, then $\varphi(t/k)$ is the characteristic function for x/k.

By Theorem VIII, Chap. 5, the density function for $u = x/k$ is $g(u) = k\,f(ku)$; so the characteristic function for u is

$$\varphi_1(t) = \int_{-\infty}^{\infty} e^{itu} k\, f(ku)\,du$$

$$= \int_{-\infty}^{\infty} e^{i(t/k)ku} f(ku) k\, du$$

$$= \varphi\left(\frac{t}{k}\right).$$

Theorem VI. The characteristic function for the normal distribution is $e^{-t^2/2}$.

This is proved by a direct computation from (1):

$$\varphi(t) = \int_{-\infty}^{\infty} \frac{1}{\sqrt{2\pi}}\, e^{itx}\, e^{-x^2/2}\, dx$$

$$= \int_{-\infty}^{\infty} \frac{1}{\sqrt{2\pi}}\, e^{-\frac{1}{2}(x^2 - 2itx)}\, dx$$

$$= \int_{-\infty}^{\infty} \frac{1}{\sqrt{2\pi}}\, e^{-\frac{1}{2}(x^2 - 2itx - t^2 + t^2)}\, dx$$

$$= e^{-t^2/2} \int_{-\infty}^{\infty} \frac{1}{\sqrt{2\pi}}\, e^{-(x - it)^2/2}\, dx$$

$$= e^{-t^2/2}.$$

67. Application to the Central Limit Theorem

Let us begin our discussion of general proofs of the central limit theorem by considering the case (Corollary 3 to Theorem I) of identical variables with second moments. Though this seems like a very special case, the student should see from the example on sample means that it is a very important one. Indeed, whatever we may be studying about samples (means or anything else), the set of sample values is a set of identical stochastic variables.

So let $x_1, x_2, x_3, \ldots$ be independent and have identical distribu-

tions with second moments.   As usual, we assume the common mean
is zero.   Instead of b_k we shall now write b inasmuch as the x_k's all
have the same variance.   Furthermore, we let $\varphi(t)$ be the characteristic function for x_k—also the same for all k's.   If we compute the first
two derivatives of φ (differentiating with respect to t under the integral
sign), we have

$$\varphi'(t) = \int_{-\infty}^{\infty} ixe^{itx} f(x)dx,$$

$$\varphi''(t) = \int_{-\infty}^{\infty} -x^2 e^{itx} f(x)dx.$$

The existence of the first two moments and the boundedness of e^{itx} tell
us that these integrals converge; so φ has two derivatives, and it can
be shown that they are continuous.   At $t = 0$, we get

$$e^{itx} = e^0 = 1;$$

so

$$\varphi(0) = \int_{-\infty}^{\infty} f(x)dx = 1,$$

$$\varphi'(0) = \int_{-\infty}^{\infty} ix f(x)dx = i\bar{x} = 0,$$

$$\varphi''(0) = \int_{-\infty}^{\infty} -x^2 f(x)dx = -b.$$

Therefore (Prob. 21, Chap. 7)

$$\varphi(t) = 1 - \frac{b}{2} t^2 + o(t^2).$$

In this problem,

$$S_n = \frac{1}{\sqrt{B_n}} \sum_{k=1}^{n} x_k = \sum_{k=1}^{n} \frac{x_k}{\sqrt{nb}};$$

so we want the characteristic function for $x_k/\sqrt{nb}$.   By **Theorem V**,
this is

$$\varphi\left(\frac{t}{\sqrt{nb}}\right) = 1 - \frac{t^2}{2n} + o\left(\frac{1}{n}\right).$$

By **Theorem IV**, the characteristic function for S_n is the nth power of
this:

$$\left[\varphi\left(\frac{t}{\sqrt{nb}}\right)\right]^n = \left[1 - \frac{t^2}{2n} + o\left(\frac{1}{n}\right)\right]^n \to e^{-t^2/2}$$

by Prob. 25, Chap. 7.   The application of Theorem VI and Theorem
III now completes the proof of the case stated in Corollary 3 to
Theorem I.

This simple case illustrates the general idea, but we might as well look at a rough outline of the Liapounoff theorem. If the x_k's are not identical, we have different characteristic functions; so we call them $\varphi_k(t)$. Proceeding as above, we get $\varphi_k(0) = 1$, $\varphi_k'(0) = i\bar{x}_k = 0$, and $\varphi_k''(0) = -b_k$. Thus, on dividing by $\sqrt{B_n}$, we have

$$\varphi_k\left(\frac{t}{\sqrt{B_n}}\right) = 1 - \frac{b_k t^2}{2B_n} + \cdots$$

So the leading term in the expansion of $\log \varphi_k$ reads

$$\log \varphi_k\left(\frac{t}{\sqrt{B_n}}\right) = -\frac{b_k t^2}{2B_n} + \cdots$$

For the characteristic function of S_n we want

$$\prod_{k=1}^{n} \varphi_k\left(\frac{t}{B_n}\right);$$

so for the logarithms we want

$$\sum_{k=1}^{n} \log \varphi_k\left(\frac{t}{\sqrt{B_n}}\right) = \sum_{k=1}^{n} -\frac{b_k t^2}{2B_n} + \cdots = -\frac{t^2}{2} + \cdots$$

because by Theorem V, Chap. 6, $B_n = \Sigma b_k$.

Again, we have the right answer provided that the error terms (carefully omitted above) behave right. The details of that argument are only tedious, but we might indicate what is called for to make the errors behave. If we assume the existence of third moments for the x_k's, we get third derivatives for φ_k; and the Maclaurin formula with remainder gives the error in the expansion of $\varphi_k(t/\sqrt{B_n})$ as $\theta c_k t^3/6B_n^{3/2}$, where $|\theta| \leq 1$ and $c_k = E(|x_k|^3)$. By some routine computation and an inequality on moments due to Liapounoff, we can get an estimate of the same order of magnitude for the error in the logarithm of φ_k. So the total error is the sum of these, and Liapounoff's hypothesis is just what we should expect—that this sum tends to zero. It might be well to state this theorem formally.

Theorem VII (*Laplace-Liapounoff*). If $x_1, x_2, x_3, \ldots$ is a sequence of independent stochastic variables, each having an absolute third moment c_k, and if

$$\lim_{n \to \infty} B_n^{-3/2} \sum_{k=1}^{n} c_k = 0,$$

then

$$\lim_{n \to \infty} pr\{a \le S_n \le b\} = \int_a^b \frac{1}{\sqrt{2\pi}}\, e^{-z^2/2}\, dz.$$

We have outlined here the proofs of two forms of the central limit theorem, that stated in Corollary 3 to Theorem I and that stated just now in Theorem VII. Though the method of attack is roughly the same for the two cases and though the first form seems much simpler, the student must not get the impression that it is a special case of Theorem VII. In the case of the identical variables we needed only second moments, whereas in the more general case that is not sufficient. The form of the central limit theorem given in Corollary 3 to Theorem I follows as a corollary from the Lindeberg theorem, but not from that of Liapounoff.

68. Example—Cauchy's Distribution

Cauchy's example of the failure of the central limit law consists of a sequence of independent variables, each having the density function

$$f(x) = \frac{1}{\pi(1 + x^2)}.$$

It turns out that the characteristic function for this distribution is

$$\varphi(t) = e^{-|t|}.$$

A direct calculation of this by (1), Sec. 66, calls for analytical techniques beyond the scope of this book, but we can at least indicate that this is the case by applying the inversion formula to $\varphi(t)$ and seeing that we get $f(x)$:

$$\frac{1}{2\pi} \int_{-\infty}^{\infty} e^{-itx}\varphi(t)dt = \frac{1}{2\pi}\left(\int_{-\infty}^{0} e^{t-itx}\, dt + \int_{0}^{\infty} e^{-t-itx}\, dt \right)$$

$$= \frac{1}{2\pi}\left(\frac{e^{t-itx}}{1-ix}\Big|_{-\infty}^{0} - \frac{e^{-t-itx}}{1+ix}\Big|_{0}^{\infty} \right)$$

$$= \frac{1}{2\pi}\left(\frac{1}{1-ix} + \frac{1}{1+ix} \right)$$

$$= \frac{1}{\pi(1 + x^2)}.$$

Now, by Theorem IV, the characteristic function for

$$\sum_{k=1}^{n} x_k$$

is

$$[\varphi(t)]^n = e^{-n|t|}.$$

Therefore, by Theorem V, the characteristic function for

$$\frac{1}{n}\sum_{k=1}^{n} x_k$$

is

$$e^{-n|t|/n} = e^{-|t|},$$

the same as that for each of the x_k's. So the arithmetic mean of the first n variables has the same distribution as that of the individual variables.

As we noted in Sec. 42, these variables do not have second moments —they do not even have first moments. So the classical formulation of the central limit law is impossible. However, the striking thing about this example is that *no* averaging process leads to a normal distribution. Let $\{\alpha_n\}$ be any sequence of constants. Then the density function for

$$\frac{1}{\alpha_n}\sum_{k=1}^{n} x_k$$

is

$$\frac{\alpha_n}{n\pi[1 + (\alpha_n x/n)^2]}$$

and under no circumstances does this tend to $(2\pi)^{-\frac{1}{2}}e^{-x^2/2}$.

69. Bernoullian Case—Detailed Proof

If the variables x_k represent a Bernoullian sequence of trials, then (see Sec. 48)

$$E\left(\sum_{k=1}^{n} x_k\right) = np,$$

$$B_n = \operatorname{var}\left(\sum_{k=1}^{n} x_k\right) = npq.$$

If, as usual, r represents the number of successes in n trials, then we have seen that

$$r = \sum_{k=1}^{n} x_k.$$

Therefore, the variables X_n and S_n of this chapter are

$$X_n = r - np,$$
$$S_n = (r - np)/\sqrt{npq}.$$

So this special case of the central limit theorem reads as follows:

Theorem VIII.   For a Bernoullian sequence of trials,

$$pr\left\{a \le \frac{r - np}{\sqrt{npq}} \le b\right\} = \int_a^b \frac{1}{\sqrt{2\pi}}\, e^{-z^2/2}\, dz + o(1).$$

The usual proof of this theorem is very straightforward.   The probability function for r is well known:

$$f(r) = {}^nC_r p^r q^{n-r}.$$

The Stirling theorem approximation to the factorials in ${}^nC_r$ and the obvious changes of variable lead us directly to the result.   Let

$$z = \frac{r - np}{\sqrt{npq}};$$

then

(1)
$$r = np + z\sqrt{npq},$$
(2)
$$n - r = nq - z\sqrt{npq}.$$

If z is bounded (and, indeed, we want $a \le z \le b$), then r and $n - r$ both tend to ∞ as n does.   So the Stirling formula applies to all three factorials:

$$f(r) = \frac{n!\,p^r q^{n-r}}{r!(n-r)!}$$

$$= \frac{n^{n+\frac{1}{2}}e^{-n}p^r q^{n-r}}{r^{r+\frac{1}{2}}e^{-r}(n-r)^{n-r+\frac{1}{2}}e^{-n+r}\sqrt{2\pi}}\,[1 + o(1)]$$

$$= \frac{1 + o(1)}{\left(\dfrac{r}{np}\right)^{r+\frac{1}{2}}\left(\dfrac{n-r}{nq}\right)^{n-r+\frac{1}{2}}\sqrt{2\pi npq}}.$$

$$\log f(r) = -\log\sqrt{2\pi npq} - \left(r + \frac{1}{2}\right)\log\left(\frac{r}{np}\right) - \left(n - r + \frac{1}{2}\right)$$
$$\log\left(\frac{n-r}{nq}\right) + o(1).$$

Now, from (1) and (2), respectively, we have

$$\frac{r}{np} = 1 + z\sqrt{\frac{q}{np}},$$

$$\frac{n-r}{nq} = 1 - z\sqrt{\frac{p}{nq}}.$$

Therefore,

$$\log f(r) = -\log \sqrt{2\pi npq} - \left(np + z\sqrt{npq} + \frac{1}{2}\right)\log\left(1 + z\sqrt{\frac{q}{np}}\right)$$
$$- \left(nq - z\sqrt{npq} + \frac{1}{2}\right)\log\left(1 - z\sqrt{\frac{p}{nq}}\right) + o(1).$$

Our next step is to expand these last two logarithms in series. Here we have direct evidence of the significance of the size of p and q. The series expansion

$$\log(1 + x) = x - \frac{x^2}{2} + \frac{x^3}{3} - \cdots$$

is convergent only for $|x| \leq 1$ and not very rapidly convergent unless $|x|$ is very small. Now, our variables, $z(q/np)^{\frac{1}{2}}$ and $-z(p/nq)^{\frac{1}{2}}$, are small for n sufficiently large; but if either p or q is very small, there should be a better approximation for intermediate values of n. This is the role played by the Poisson formula—see Chap. 10.

Our present concern is with the limit theorem, however; and to this end we note that, for n sufficiently large, the series expansions are valid and we have

$$\log f(r) = -\log \sqrt{2\pi npq}$$
$$- \left(np + z\sqrt{npq} + \frac{1}{2}\right)\left[z\sqrt{\frac{q}{np}} - \frac{z^2 q}{2np} + O(n^{-\frac{3}{2}})\right]$$
$$- \left(nq - z\sqrt{npq} + \frac{1}{2}\right)\left[-z\sqrt{\frac{p}{nq}} - \frac{z^2 p}{2nq} + O(n^{-\frac{3}{2}})\right] + o(1)$$
$$= -\log \sqrt{\pi 2npq} - \frac{z^2}{2} + o(1).$$

So

(3) $$f(r) = \frac{1}{\sqrt{2\pi npq}} e^{-z^2/2}[1 + o(1)].$$

As r runs through integer values, the increments in z are $(npq)^{-\frac{1}{2}}$; therefore we could write

$$f(r) = \frac{1}{\sqrt{2\pi}} e^{-z^2/2} \Delta z[1 + o(1)].$$

Now, as $n \to \infty$, $\Delta z \to 0$; so

$$pr\{a \leq z \leq b\} = \sum_{z \geq a}^{z \leq b} \left(\frac{1}{\sqrt{2\pi}} e^{-z^2/2} \Delta z[1 + o(1)]\right)$$
$$= \int_a^b \frac{1}{\sqrt{2\pi}} e^{-z^2/2}\, dz + o(1) + \sum o(1)e^{-z^2/2} \Delta z.$$

The error term in (3) depends on z, but for $a \leq z \leq b$ it is bounded, and its upper bound tends to zero as $n \to \infty$; therefore we can write

$$\left| \Sigma e^{-z^2/2} \, \Delta z \, o(1) \right| \leq \left| \Sigma e^{-z^2/2} \, \Delta z \right| o(1) = o(1),$$

whence

(4) $$pr\{a \leq z \leq b\} = \int_a^b \frac{1}{\sqrt{2\pi}} \, e^{-z^2/2} \, dz + o(1).$$

This proves the limit theorem. It also furnishes us with the proof promised in Chap. 7 that the constant in Stirling's theorem is $\sqrt{2\pi}$. The logarithm of the coefficient of $e^{-z^2/2}$ in (4) is just the negative of the constant C_2 of (3), Sec. 53. To make the integral of the density function in (4) unity, we must have this coefficient equal to $1/\sqrt{2\pi}$; therefore $C_2 = \log \sqrt{2\pi}$.

The question of the error term in (4) is a rather complicated one. The proof we have given of Theorem VIII (basically that of de Moivre) does not lead to anything very interesting in the way of an estimate of this error. Uspensky (*Introduction to Mathematical Probability*, Chap. VII) has adapted Laplace's proof of Theorem VIII to get such an estimate. Rather than attempt any such procedure here, let us turn our attention to (3) and the error involved there. Equation (3) gives us an approximation to the probability for a single value of r. The Poisson formula (Chap. 10) gives another approximation to the same thing. So the most direct comparison of the normal law with the Poisson law is given by comparing the error in (3) with the error term in Theorem III, Chap. 10.

Feller has pointed out that (3) does not give the best first-order approximation to $f(r)$. The form of (3) is, of course, suggested by the classical formulation of the central limit law. What Feller suggests is that instead of the variable

$$z = \frac{r - np}{\sqrt{npq}},$$

we consider the variable

$$u = \frac{r - (n+1)p + \frac{1}{2}}{\sqrt{(n+1)pq}}.$$

This leads to the same limit theorem, but the error in the approximation

$$f(r) \simeq \frac{e^{-u^2/2}}{\sqrt{2\pi(n+1)pq}}$$

is much neater than that in (3). We present here a slight modification of Feller's argument:

Theorem IX. The probability of r successes in n Bernoullian trials is approximately

$$[2\pi(n+1)pq]^{-\frac{1}{2}} \exp\left(\frac{-[r-(n+1)p+\frac{1}{2}]^2}{2(n+1)pq}\right).$$

The ratio of the correct result to this approximation is

$$\exp\left[+\frac{(q-p)u^3}{6\sqrt{(n+1)pq}} - \frac{(p^3+q^3)u^4}{3(n+1)pq} + \frac{u^4 Q}{4(n+1)pq} + R\right]$$

where

$$u = \frac{r-(n+1)p+\frac{1}{2}}{\sqrt{(n+1)pq}},$$

$$Q = \frac{q^3\theta_1}{\left(1+u\sqrt{\dfrac{q}{(n+1)p}}\right)^3} + \frac{p^3\theta_2}{\left(1-u\sqrt{\dfrac{p}{(n+1)q}}\right)^3},$$

$$0 < \theta_1 < 1, \qquad 0 < \theta_2 < 1,$$

and

$$|R| < \frac{1}{24[(n+1)pq + u(q-p)\sqrt{(n+1)pq} + u^2 pq]} + \frac{1}{12n+18}.$$

The proof of this theorem parallels very closely the proof we have given for Theorem VIII. Instead of giving all the details of computation here, let us merely refer back to the steps in the proof of Theorem VIII and indicate the changes to be made. In place of (1) and (2) we have

$$(5) \qquad r + \frac{1}{2} = (n+1)p + u\sqrt{(n+1)pq}$$

$$= (n+1)p\left(1 + u\sqrt{\frac{q}{(n+1)p}}\right),$$

$$(6) \quad n - r + \frac{1}{2} = (n+1)q - u\sqrt{(n+1)pq}$$

$$= (n+1)q\left(1 - u\sqrt{\frac{p}{(n+1)q}}\right).$$

Before applying Stirling's formula to $f(r)$, we multiply and divide by $n+1$ to get

$$f(r) = \frac{(n+1)!p^r q^{n-r}}{(n+1)r!(n-r)!}.$$

Now, for $(n+1)!$ we use Stirling's formula as given by Theorem I, Chap. 7. For $r!$ and $(n-r)!$ we use the form given in Prob. 9, Chap.

7.   The resulting approximation to $f(r)$ then simplifies to

$$\frac{1}{\sqrt{2\pi(n+1)pq}\left[\dfrac{r+\frac{1}{2}}{(n+1)p}\right]^{r+\frac{1}{2}}\left[\dfrac{n-r+\frac{1}{2}}{(n+1)q}\right]^{n-r+\frac{1}{2}}}$$

Now, we take logarithms and substitute from (5) and (6).

$$\log f(r) \simeq -\log \sqrt{2\pi(n+1)pq}$$
$$- (n+1)p\left(1 + u\sqrt{\frac{q}{(n+1)p}}\right)\log\left(1 + u\sqrt{\frac{q}{(n+1)p}}\right)$$
$$- (n+1)q\left(1 - u\sqrt{\frac{p}{(n+1)q}}\right)\log\left(1 - u\sqrt{\frac{p}{(n+1)q}}\right).$$

At this stage, we can see why this seemingly more complicated form of the problem leads to a simpler and more efficient estimate of the error term.   In the proof of Theorem VIII, we used a series expansion for something of the form $(1 + x + y)\log(1 + x)$.   Here, it is simplified to the form $(1 + x)\log(1 + x)$.   The Maclaurin formula with remainder gives

$$\log(1 + x) = x - \frac{x^2}{2} + \frac{x^3}{3} - \frac{\theta x^4}{4(1+x)^4} \quad (0 < \theta < 1).$$

Therefore

$$(7)\qquad (1 + x)\log(1 + x) = x + \frac{x^2}{2} - \frac{x^3}{6} + \frac{x^4}{3} - \frac{\theta x^4}{4(1+x)^3}.$$

It is now only a matter of routine computation to complete the proof of Theorem IX.   We use (7) twice, first with

$$x = u\sqrt{\frac{q}{(n+1)p}},$$

then with

$$x = -u\sqrt{\frac{p}{(n+1)q}}.$$

Then, we multiply by $-(n+1)p$ and $-(n+1)q$, respectively, and add.   The first-degree terms cancel; the second-degree terms give us $-u^2/2$; and the other three terms in (7) give us the first three terms, respectively, in the error in the logarithm.   Finally, the error term designated by R is that due to the Stirling approximation.   The bound on it is computed directly from (1), Sec. 53, and Prob. 10, Chap. 7.

We shall have more to say about Theorem IX in the next chapter where we compare it with the Poisson approximation.   There is only one point we should like to make here.   The leading logarithmic error term is

$$\frac{(q - p)u^3}{6 \sqrt{(n + 1)pq}},$$

which means that in general for fixed (or at least bounded) u the logarithmic error is $O(n^{-1/2})$. However, all the other terms in the error are $O(n^{-1})$; and for the one special case $p = q = \frac{1}{2}$ the leading term vanishes. Therefore, for $p = \frac{1}{2}$, not only is the logarithmic error smaller than otherwise; it is an infinitesimal of a higher order. The student should note this observation cuts two ways: (1) The central limit law approximation is best in the Bernoullian case for $p = \frac{1}{2}$. (2) Estimates of the error for $p = \frac{1}{2}$ are of no significance at all for other values of p; they are of the wrong order of magnitude.

REFERENCES FOR FURTHER STUDY

Cramér, *Mathematical Methods of Statistics*, Chaps. 15–17.
Feller, "On the Normal Approximation to the Binomial Distribution,"
    Ann. Math. Stat., vol. 16, pp. 319–329, 1945.
Levy and Roth, *Elements of Probability*, Chap. V.
Uspensky, *Introduction to Mathematical Probability*, Chaps. XIV, XV.

PROBLEMS

1. Unit electrical charges are placed at the integer points on the positive half of the real line. A unit negative charge is placed at the origin. By the inverse square law, the force on the charge at the origin due to the charge at the point k is $\pm 1/k^2$—the direction of the force depending on whether the charge at k is positive or negative. The signs of the charges at the positive integer points are chosen independently with probability $\frac{1}{2}$ for each sign at each point. The total force on the charge at the origin is the sum of the forces due to the individual charges, but the probability distribution for this total force is not normal. Show that the Lindeberg condition fails because of Corollary 1 to Theorem I.

2. Suppose the unit charges of random sign are placed, not at the integer points, but at the points $\sqrt{k}$—other conditions the same as in Prob. 1. Show that Corollary 2 to Theorem I now applies to give a normal probability distribution for the total force.

3. Show that the Lindeberg condition is satisfied by the variables in Prob. 14, Chap. 8. It now follows (as noted there) that the central limit law holds for these variables but the weak law of large numbers does not.

4. In Probs. 3, 8, and 12, Chap. 8, we asked the student to state the central limit law for each of three different sequences of variables. Verify by Corollary 3 to Theorem I that each of these sequences obeys the law.

5. In Prob. 5, Chap. 8, we asked for a statement of the central limit law for a Poisson sequence of trials. The law does not always hold in this case. Use Corollary 2 to Theorem I to find conditions under which it does hold. *Ans.* $\Sigma p_i q_i = \infty$. (See also Probs. 21, 22 below.)

6. There is a sequence of urns U_1, U_2, U_3, ... The urn U_k contains 1 white ball and $k - 1$ black balls. One ball is drawn from U_1, then one from U_2, etc. Show that the probability distribution for the number of white balls in n draws is asymptotically normal.

7. With the set of urns in Prob. 6, 2 draws (with replacement) are made from each urn, and success for each urn is defined as 2 white balls drawn. Show that the probability distribution for the number of successes is not asymptotically normal in this case.

8. From Prob. 4 above and Prob. 12, Chap. 8, it follows that, as the number m of degrees of freedom increases, the distribution of

$$\frac{\chi^2 - m}{\sqrt{2m}}$$

tends to the normal. From this derive R. A. Fisher's substitute for the χ^2 test when m is large. According to Fisher, for large m,

$$\sqrt{2\chi^2} - \sqrt{2m - 1}$$

is approximately normally distributed with variance unity. Hint:

$$\sqrt{2\chi^2} \leq \sqrt{2m - 1} + z$$

is equivalent to

$$\chi^2 \leq m - \frac{1}{2} + z\sqrt{2m - 1} + \frac{z^2}{2}.$$

As $m \to \infty$, this last expression is asymptotic to $m + z\sqrt{2m}$; therefore

$$pr\left\{\frac{\chi^2 - m}{\sqrt{2m}} \leq z\right\} \sim pr\{\sqrt{2\chi^2} \leq \sqrt{2m - 1} + z\}.$$

9. Suppose the size of an organism is due to the effect of a large number of independent random impulses x_1, x_2, ..., x_n acting on it in that order during its lifetime. Suppose, however, that the effect of a given impulse depends not only on the magnitude of the impulse but on the size of the organism at the time of the impulse. In particular, let

Z_k be the size achieved after the kth impulse and assume

$$Z_k = Z_{k-1} + x_k Z_{k-1}.$$

Then,

$$\sum_{k=1}^{n} x_k = \sum_{k=1}^{n} \frac{Z_k - Z_{k-1}}{Z_{k-1}} \simeq \int_{Z_0}^{Z_n} \frac{dZ}{Z}.$$

Assuming $Z_0 = 1$, show that the final size Z_n of the organism should have an approximately logarithmiconormal distribution. Hint: See Prob. 24, Chap. 5.

10. Individual incomes (within certain ranges) follow a reasonable facsimile of a logarithmiconormal distribution.   Devise an explanation for this modeled after the argument in Prob. 9.

11. By applying the central limit theorem to a sequence of variables each of which has a Poisson distribution, prove the following asymptotic estimate for partial sums from the exponential series: For large α,

$$\sum_{k \geq \alpha + t_1 \sqrt{\alpha}}^{k \leq \alpha + t_2 \sqrt{\alpha}} \frac{\alpha^k}{k!} \simeq e^\alpha \int_{t_1}^{t_2} \frac{1}{\sqrt{2\pi}} e^{-x^2/2} \, dx.$$

Hint: In Prob. 8, Chap. 8, substitute $\alpha = na$, $k = na + z\sqrt{na}$.

12. In Chap. 4 we described a random walk in one dimension in terms of a sequence of stochastic variables. Show that the central limit theorem applies to these variables to give the result that after a large number n of jumps

$$pr\{a \leq x \leq b\} \simeq \int_{a/\sqrt{n}}^{b/\sqrt{n}} \frac{1}{\sqrt{2\pi}} e^{-z^2/2} \, dz.$$

13. Find the effect of a translation on the characteristic function.
   Ans. If $\varphi(t)$ is the characteristic function for x, that for $x - a$ is $e^{-ita}\varphi(t)$.

14. Let $x = z - \bar{z}$, where z is the number of successes in a single Bernoullian trial. Show that the characteristic function for x is

$$qe^{-ipt} + pe^{iqt} = 1 - \frac{pqt^2}{2} + O(t^3).$$

15. From the result in Prob. 14 show that the characteristic function for S_n in a sequence of Bernoullian trials may be written

$$\left[1 - \frac{t^2}{2n} + O(n^{-3/2})\right]^n.$$

16. Apply Prob. 25, Chap. 7, to the result of Prob. 15 above to prove the central limit theorem for Bernoullian trials.

17. Let x be chosen at random between $-\frac{1}{2}$ and $\frac{1}{2}$. Find the characteristic function for x. $Ans.$ $\varphi(t) = (2/t) \sin (t/2)$.

18. Prove the central limit theorem for a sequence of independent variables, each distributed as in Prob. 17. Hint: Show that the characteristic function for S_n is

$$\left[\frac{\sqrt{n} \sin (t \sqrt{3}/\sqrt{n})}{t \sqrt{3}} \right]^n = \left[1 - \frac{t^2}{2n} + O(n^{-2}) \right]^n.$$

19. Let x have the density function $e^{-x} (x \geq 0)$. Find the characteristic function for $x - \bar{x}$. $Ans.$ $\varphi(t) = e^{-it}/(1 - it)$.

20. Prove the central limit theorem for a sequence of independent variables, each having the distribution given in Prob. 19.

21. Show that, if x_k represents one of a Poisson sequence of trials, the absolute third moment of x_k about its mean is $p_k q_k (p_k^2 + q_k^2) \leq p_k q_k$.

22. Show from Prob. 21 that, for a Poisson sequence of trials,

$$B_n^{-3/2} \sum_{k=1}^{n} c_k \leq \left(\sum_{k=1}^{n} p_k q_k \right)^{-1/2};$$

therefore the Liapounoff theorem gives the same result for this case as the Lindeberg theorem does. (Compare Prob. 5 above.)

23. Find the logarithmic error term of order $n^{-1/2}$ in the approximation (3), Sec. 69. Note that to get all terms of order $n^{-1/2}$, we must carry the Maclaurin expansions for the logarithms—immediately preceding (3)—one step farther than they are carried in the text.
                $Ans.$ $(q - p)(z^3 - 3z)/6 \sqrt{npq}$.

24. Compare the result in Prob. 23 with the error term of the same order in Theorem IX.

$Ans.$ Designating by ϵ the answer to Prob. 23 and by η the error term of order $n^{-1/2}$ in Theorem IX, we have, for $z = 1$, $|\eta| \simeq |\epsilon|/2$; for $z = \frac{1}{2}$, $|\eta| \simeq |\epsilon|/11$. However, for $z = \sqrt{3}$, $|\epsilon| = 0$; and, for (roughly) $|z| \geq \sqrt{\frac{3}{2}}$, $|\epsilon| \leq |\eta|$.

25. Noting the signs of the first two error terms in Theorem IX, show that, if $p > \frac{1}{2}$, the approximation is better for $u < 0$, while if $p < \frac{1}{2}$, it is better for $u > 0$.

26. Show that if $.1 \leq p \leq .9$ and $n \geq 1{,}000$, the logarithmic error in Theorem IX is given correct to two decimal places by the first term alone.

27. Find the probability that in 2,500 Bernoullian trials with $p = \frac{1}{2}$ the experimental ratio r/n will be within .02 of p. Answer the same question if $p = \frac{1}{3}$. *Ans.* .9544, .967.

28. In 2,500 Bernoullian trials with $p = \frac{1}{2}$ what is the best upper bound on $|(r/n) - p|$ that can be obtained with probability .95? with probability .68? *Ans.* .02, .01.

29. Answer the questions in Prob. 28 for the case $p = \frac{1}{3}$.

Ans. .019, .0095.

30. In a Bernoullian sequence of trials with $p = \frac{1}{2}$ how many trials does it take to have $|(r/n) - p| < .01$ with probability .95? with probability .68? *Ans.* 10,000; 2,500.

31. Answer the questions in Prob. 30 for the case $p = \frac{1}{3}$.

Ans. 8,800, 2,200.

CHAPTER 10

THE POISSON DISTRIBUTION

In this chapter we want to present two important interpretations of the Poisson probability function $a^r e^{-a}/r!$. One is that it furnishes an approximation to Bernoullian probabilities for the case of small p. This is the classical interpretation, and we shall investigate it at some length, determining how good an approximation the Poisson formula furnishes and comparing it with the normal law approximation (Theorem IX, Chap. 9). However, in the modern theory of probability there is another interpretation in which the Poisson distribution appears as the exact solution to a certain general type of problem. To get a representative picture, the student should see this point of view too, and it is presented in Theorem IV.

The examples in the chapter and those among the problems at the end should give the student some idea of the importance of the Poisson distribution, but we might add that there are other topics in the modern theory of probability not even mentioned in this book in which the Poisson formula plays an important role.

70. The Binomial Limit

As we indicated in Chap. 8, the Poisson probability function appears as the limit of the sequence of pseudo-Bernoullian probability functions (1), Sec. 57. That fact and a slight generalization of it can serve as the basis for both of the developments we want to present in this chapter; so we first turn our attention to the proof that the sequence (1), Sec. 57, obeys the Poisson limit law.

Theorem I. If a is a constant and r is a fixed positive integer,

$$\lim_{n \to \infty} {}_nC_r \left(\frac{a}{n}\right)^r \left(1 - \frac{a}{n}\right)^{n-r} = \frac{a^r e^{-a}}{r!}.$$

All this requires is straightforward computation:

$$
{}_nC_r \left(\frac{a}{n}\right)^r \left(1 - \frac{a}{n}\right)^{n-r} = \frac{n! a^r \left(1 - \dfrac{a}{n}\right)^n}{r!(n - r)! n^r \left(1 - \dfrac{a}{n}\right)^r}
$$

$$= \frac{a^r \left(1 - \dfrac{a}{n}\right)^n}{r!} \cdot \frac{n(n-1) \cdots (n-r+1)}{n^r \left(1 - \dfrac{a}{n}\right)^r}$$

$$= \frac{a^r \left(1 - \dfrac{a}{n}\right)^n}{r!} \cdot \frac{1\left(1 - \dfrac{1}{n}\right) \cdots \left(1 - \dfrac{r-1}{n}\right)}{\left(1 - \dfrac{a}{n}\right)^r}.$$

Now,

$$\left(1 - \frac{a}{n}\right)^n \rightarrow e^{-a},$$

and in the second fraction there are a fixed number r of factors in both numerator and denominator with each factor tending to unity. Therefore, this entire fraction tends to unity, and the theorem is proved.

In order to present the fundamental steps with a minimum of confusion, we assumed in Theorem I that a was a constant. Actually, the same result (with the same proof) holds if we replace a by a variable which tends to a as $n \rightarrow \infty$. In other words, in place of a, write $a + o(1)$; in place of a/n, write $(a/n) + o(1/n)$. We leave it to the student to check that this does not affect the above argument, and we list for reference the following:

Theorem II. As $n \rightarrow \infty$,

$$_nC_r \left[\frac{a}{n} + o\left(\frac{1}{n}\right)\right]^r \left[1 - \frac{a}{n} + o\left(\frac{1}{n}\right)\right]^{n-r} = \frac{a^r e^{-a}}{r!} + o(1).$$

71. Approximation to Bernoullian Probabilities

It is a good idea to have an estimate of the error in any approximation formula; but this seems particularly desirable here, because the Poisson formula is used as a substitute for the central limit law in the case of Bernoullian trials with small p. To find out just when we should change formulas, we need an estimate of the error in each case. We have already obtained this estimate for the central limit law, and now we want to do the same for the Poisson law.

Theorem III. If r is a positive integer and $a > 0$, then

$$_nC_r \left(\frac{a}{n}\right)^r \left(1 - \frac{a}{n}\right)^{n-r} = \frac{a^r e^{-a}}{r!} \exp\left[\frac{r - (a-r)^2}{2n} + \frac{r(a^2 - r^2)}{2n^2} + R\right]$$

where

$$|R| < \frac{r^2(4r+3)}{12(n-r)^2} + \frac{a^3(n-r)}{3(n-a)^3}.$$

Let us write

$$\frac{n!\left(\frac{a}{n}\right)^r\left(1-\frac{a}{n}\right)^{n-r}}{r!(n-r)!} = \frac{a^r e^{-a}}{r!}e^Q.$$

Then,

$$e^Q = \frac{e^a n![1-(a/n)]^{n-r}}{n^r(n-r)!}.$$

On applying Stirling's formula, we have

$$e^Q = \frac{e^a n^{n+\frac{1}{2}}e^{-n}\left(1-\dfrac{a}{n}\right)^{n-r}e^{\epsilon_n}}{n^r(n-r)^{n-r+\frac{1}{2}}e^{r-n}e^{\epsilon_{n-r}}}$$

$$= \frac{e^{a-r}\left(1-\dfrac{a}{n}\right)^{n-r}e^{\epsilon_n}}{\left(1-\dfrac{r}{n}\right)^{n-r+\frac{1}{2}}e^{\epsilon_{n-r}}};$$

therefore

$$(1)\quad Q = a - r + (n-r)\log\left(1-\frac{a}{n}\right) - (n-r)\log\left(1-\frac{r}{n}\right)$$
$$- \frac{1}{2}\log\left(1-\frac{r}{n}\right) - \epsilon$$

where

$$\epsilon = \epsilon_{n-r} - \epsilon_n.$$

We apply (1), Sec. 53, taking the smaller estimate for ϵ_{n-r} and the larger estimate for ϵ_n, and have

$$(2)\quad 0 < \epsilon < \frac{1}{12(n-r)} - \frac{1}{12(n+\frac{1}{2})} = \frac{2r+1}{12(n-r)(2n+1)}.$$

Next, we expand the logarithms in series. In each case we have something of the form $\log(1-x)$, where $0 < x < 1$. The Maclaurin formula with remainder tells us that, if we carry such an expansion through the term in x^{k-1}, the remainder is

$$\frac{x^k}{k!}\frac{d^k}{dt^k}\log(1-t) = \frac{-x^k}{k(1-t)^k}.$$

where $0 < t < x$. Clearly, such remainders are negative and less in absolute value than

$$\frac{x^k}{k(1-x)^k}.$$

Bearing this in mind we write

$$(n-r)\log\left(1-\frac{a}{n}\right) = (n-r)\left(-\frac{a}{n}-\frac{a^2}{2n^2}-\delta'\right)$$

(3)
$$= -a - \frac{a^2-2ar}{2n} + \frac{a^2r}{2n^2} - \delta$$

where

(4) $$0 < \delta = (n-r)\delta' < \frac{a^3(n-r)}{3n^3\left(1-\dfrac{a}{n}\right)^3} = \frac{a^3(n-r)}{3(n-a)^3}.$$

Similarly,

$$-(n-r)\log\left(1-\frac{r}{n}\right) = (n-r)\left(\frac{r}{n}+\frac{r}{2n^2}+\eta'\right)$$

(5)
$$= r - \frac{r^2}{2n} - \frac{r^3}{2n^2} + \eta$$

where

(6) $$0 < \eta = (n-r)\eta' < \frac{r^3(n-r)}{3n^3\left(1-\dfrac{r}{n}\right)^3} = \frac{r^3}{3(n-r)^2}.$$

Finally,

(7) $$-\frac{1}{2}\log\left(1-\frac{r}{n}\right) = \frac{r}{2n} + \tau$$

where

(8) $$0 < \tau < \frac{1}{2}\frac{r^2}{2n^2\left(1-\dfrac{r}{n}\right)^2} = \frac{r^2}{4(n-r)^2}.$$

Substituting (3), (5), and (7) in (1), we have

$$Q = \frac{r-(a-r)^2}{2n} + \frac{r(a^2-r^2)}{2n^2} - \epsilon - \delta + \eta + \tau.$$

This completes the proof except for the estimate of R. It is easily seen that

$$\frac{2r+1}{12(n-r)(2n+1)} < \frac{r^2(3r+4)}{12(n-r)^2};$$

so by (2)
$$0 < \epsilon < \frac{r^2(3r+4)}{12(n-r)^2}.$$

However, from (6) and (8) we have
$$0 < \eta + \tau < \frac{r^2(3r+4)}{12(n-r)^2}.$$

Therefore,
$$|\eta + \tau - \epsilon| < \frac{r^2(3r+4)}{12(n-r)^2}.$$

Now, we bring in (4) and have
$$|R| = |\eta + \tau - \epsilon - \delta| \le |\eta + \tau - \epsilon| + |\delta| < \frac{r^2(3r+4)}{12(n-r)^2} + \frac{a^3(n-r)}{3(n-a)^3}.$$

This completes the proof of Theorem III.

Corollary 1. The probability of r successes in n Bernoullian trials is approximately
$$\frac{(np)^r e^{-np}}{r!}.$$

The ratio of the correct result to this approximation is
$$\exp\left(\frac{rp^2}{2} - \frac{(r-np)^2}{2n} + \frac{r}{2n} - \frac{r^3}{2n^2} + R\right)$$
where
$$|R| < \frac{r^2(3r+4)}{12(n-r)^2} + \frac{1}{3}(n-r)\left(\frac{p}{q}\right)^3.$$

This follows immediately from Theorem III by substituting $a = np$.

72. Comparison with the Normal Law

The estimates of error given in Theorem IX, Chap. 9, and Corollary 1 above enable us to tell, for any given problem, how accurate each approximation is. So if we have a problem in which there is some doubt as to which formula we should use, the best thing to do is to compute the error for each one and see which is the more accurate. However, it is a good idea to have in mind a general description of the type of problem to which each formula is applicable. The purpose of this section is to give the student some such general description.

In each case we have described the error by giving the ratio of the correct result to the approximation in the form of an exponential. This is a very convenient form for reading off relative errors. The approximation
$$e^z \simeq 1 + z$$

indicates that the exponent should give us a good idea of the relative error. For numbers that we should expect to find in error terms, this approximation is really quite satisfactory. For instance, $e^{.1} = 1.105$, $e^{.05} = 1.051$, $e^{.01} = 1.01005$. So, in studying these error terms, we shall compute the exponent and call that the relative error.

For any Bernoullian sequence the normal law approximation gets better as n increases; so the natural way to describe its applicability is to find a minimum n for a given degree of accuracy in each situation. The accuracy of the normal law depends on the values of u and p as well as on the value of n. It is natural to speak of the value of u rather than that of r—though, of course, we have to compute u from r, n, and p—because the tables of values of the normal distribution function are always in terms of u. We include here a few computations from the error term in Theorem IX, Chap. 9, for $u = 1$ and $u = 2$ —that is, for r one and two standard deviations from its mean. Values of p are given at the left. The desired degree of accuracy is given at the top. The entries in the table are (rounded off) minimum values of n.

TABLE I.   NUMBER OF TRIALS REQUIRED FOR GIVEN ACCURACY OF NORMAL LAW
($u = 1$)

p	10%	5%	1%	0.1%
.5	2	4	20	200
.4	3	5	50	5,000
.3	4	10	225	22,500
.2	7	25	650	65,000
.1	20	80	2,000	200,000
.05	50	200	5,000	500,000
.01	300	1,200	30,000	3,000,000

TABLE II.   NUMBER OF TRIALS REQUIRED FOR GIVEN ACCURACY OF NORMAL LAW
($u = 2$)

p	10%	5%	1%	0.1%
.5	30	60	300	3,000
.4	35	140	3,200	320,000
.3	150	600	15,000	1,500,000
.2	400	1,600	40,000	4,000,000
.1	1,300	5,200	130,000	13,000,000
.05	3,200	13,000	320,000	32,000,000
.01	20,000	80,000	2,000,000	200,000,000

In the case of the Poisson law, the situation is somewhat different. This is not an asymptotic formula for Bernoullian probabilities; so there is a maximum n in each case as well as a minimum.   In addition to the restrictions imposed by the question of accuracy, there is the practical consideration of the usefulness of the formula itself.   If np is too large, values of r near the mean will be too large for the formula to be practical.   There is an excellent set of tables of values of the Poisson approximation in Molina's *Poisson's Exponential Binomial Limit*, New York (1942).   These tables are for values of $a(= np)$ from .001 through 100.   Let us take this as the range of usefulness of the formula.   There still remains the question of accuracy; and this depends on n, p, and the deviation $|r - np|$.   Tables III and IV give

TABLE III.   NUMBER OF TRIALS REQUIRED FOR GIVEN ACCURACY OF POISSON LAW
($|r - np| = 5$)

p	10%	5%	1%	0.1%
.1	150–200	—	—	—
.05	125–1,000	300–700	—	—
.01	125+	250+	1,250+	—
.001	125+	250+	1,250+	12,500+
.0001	*	*	1,250+	12,500+
.00001	*	*	1,250+	12,500+

TABLE IV.   NUMBER OF TRIALS REQUIRED FOR GIVEN ACCURACY OF POISSON LAW
($|r - np| = 10$)

p	10%	5%	1%	0.1%
.1	—	—	—	—
.05	600–1,000	—	—	—
.01	500+	1,000+	6,000+	—
.001	500+	1,000+	5,000+	50,000+
.0001	*	1,000+	5,000+	50,000+
.00001	*	*	5,000+	50,000+

estimates from Corollary 1 to Theorem III in accordance with the following conventions: In some cases the indicated degree of accuracy cannot be attained; we have marked these with a dash (—).   In some cases there are both upper and lower limits for n within the range of Molina's tables; for these we give both limits.   In some cases there is a lower limit that should be noted while the upper limit is beyond the range of Molina's tables; for these we give the lower limit followed by a plus $(+)$. Finally, in some cases the indicated degree of accuracy is guaranteed for all applicable entries in Molina's tables; we have marked these situations with an asterisk $(*)$.

73. Example—Telephone Trunk Lines

Suppose a large corporation is planning to have a PBX telephone system installed. They will have a fairly large number n of individual telephones, but each will connect into the company switchboard, and not nearly so many outside lines will be required. If data are available on the average proportion of the time each telephone is in use for outside calls, we can make a good guess as to the number of trunk lines needed for efficient service. Let p be the probability that an individual telephone is using an outside line at a given time. To estimate such a probability, we set $60p$ equal to the average number of minutes per hour per telephone spent on outside calls.

Now, we think of the n phones as n independent "trials." Each trial consists of the question of whether or not a certain telephone requires an outside line at a certain time. The variable r (which we ordinarily think of as the number of "successes") then represents the number of trunk lines in demand at a given time. The service should be reasonably efficient if the probability is fairly large (say .95) that the number r of lines in demand does not exceed the number available. That is, if k is the number of lines to be installed, we want

$$pr\{r \leq k\} \geq .95.$$

To estimate this probability from the normal law, we note that $r \leq k$ means

$$\frac{r - np}{\sqrt{npq}} \leq \frac{k - np}{\sqrt{npq}};$$

and the probability of this latter inequality is approximately

$$\frac{1}{\sqrt{2\pi}} \int_{-\infty}^{(k-np)/\sqrt{npq}} e^{-z^2/2}\, dz.$$

According to a table of the normal distribution, this integral is .95 if the upper limit is 1.65. Therefore, we get approximately 95 per cent efficiency if the number of trunk lines is

$$k = np + 1.65 \sqrt{npq}.$$

In general, p is rather small in this problem; so we could hope to get a reasonable estimate from the Poisson formula. This procedure involves choosing k so that

$$e^{-np} \sum_{r=k+1}^{\infty} \frac{(np)^r}{r!} \leq .05.$$

The telephone engineers prefer this solution to the problem because it requires no computation. Molina's tables include a section on cumulative probabilities such as the one above, and the required value of k can be read off directly from the tables.

74. Example—Counting Bacteria

To count the bacteria in a given culture the usual procedure is to dilute the substance in which they are contained until a single drop of the mixture will contain on the average so few bacteria that they can be counted by direct observation under the microscope. If we keep track of the proportions used in diluting and the size of the drops studied, a little simple arithmetic takes us back from the average count per drop to the count per unit volume in the original culture.

The point that interests us here is that there is a Poisson probability distribution for the number of bacteria observed in a single drop under the microscope. We let the individual bacteria represent "trials" with success defined as "contained in the drop under observation." Clearly, the probability of success on a single trial is extremely small—small enough for the Poisson approximation to be very accurate. The probability of being in the drop is apparently the same for each of the bacteria; and if we assume that the probability of success for a single bacterium is independent of the presence or absence of others in the drop, we have a Bernoullian sequence of trials, and Corollary 1 to Theorem III gives us the result.

These remarks furnish a test of the bacteriologist's experimental technique. The record of a large number of observations should show an essentially Poisson frequency distribution for the count on a single observation. Otherwise, the procedure used in mixing and selecting a drop would be open to question.

75. Exact Poisson Distributions

One of the most profitable uses of the Poisson probability function is found in problems concerning the probability of occurrence of a given number of events of a certain type within a given time interval. For problems of this kind we can formulate some rather general hypotheses from which it will follow that the Poisson distribution is the actual distribution, not merely an approximation.

Suppose we are interested in the occurrence within a given time interval of events of a certain type (*e.g.*, disintegrations of atoms in a given radioactive source or claims against an insurance company). Let us distinguish three different possibilities:

(a) Exactly one event of the given type within the given time t. The probability of this we shall designate by $p(t)$.

(b) No events of the given type within the given time t. The probability of this we shall designate by $q(t)$.

(c) More than one event of the given type within the given time t. The probability of this, we shall designate by $\epsilon(t)$.

Let us now make the following hypotheses—not necessarily provable in any particular application, but certainly eminently reasonable:

(1) The probabilities p, q, and ϵ depend (as indicated by the notation) only on the duration of the time interval, not on the time it begins.

(2) For disjoint time intervals the occurrence of (a), (b), or (c) in one interval is independent of the results in the other intervals.

(3) $q(0) = 1$, and q has a continuous derivative with $q'(0) = -a$. Note that intuitively this says that in time zero we expect no events, and as t increases, the probability of no events decreases.

(4) $\epsilon(t) = o(t)$ as $t \to 0$.

Theorem IV. Subject to the hypotheses (1), (2), (3), and (4) above, the probability of exactly r events within a time interval of length t is

$$P(r) = \frac{(at)^r e^{-at}}{r!}.$$

Let us divide the given time interval into n disjoint subintervals, each of length t/n. The probability that r of these subintervals will contain one event each and the others none follows [because of hypotheses (1) and (2)] the Bernoulli formula. The only other way to get r events is to have more than one in some subinterval. The probability of this latter possibility is, by hypothesis (4), $o(1/n)$ for each subinterval, therefore less than or equal to $n \cdot o(1/n) = o(1)$ for at least one. Thus,

$$P(r) = {}^nC_r \left[p\left(\frac{t}{n}\right) \right]^r \left[q\left(\frac{t}{n}\right) \right]^{n-r} + o(1).$$

Now all we have to do is note that by hypothesis (3) and Prob. 21, Chap. 7,

$$q\left(\frac{t}{n}\right) = 1 - \frac{at}{n} + o\left(\frac{1}{n}\right);$$

therefore

$$p\left(\frac{t}{n}\right) = 1 - q\left(\frac{t}{n}\right) - \epsilon\left(\frac{t}{n}\right)$$

$$= \frac{at}{n} + o\left(\frac{1}{n}\right).$$

and we have

$$P(r) = {}_nC_r\left[\frac{at}{n} + o\left(\frac{1}{n}\right)\right]^r\left[1 - \frac{at}{n} + o\left(\frac{1}{n}\right)\right]^{n-r} + o(1).$$

With the unspecified o functions properly chosen, this holds for each n; thus it holds for the limit as $n \to \infty$, and the desired result follows from Theorem II.

76. Example—Radioactive Disintegrations

The emission of α particles by a radioactive source furnishes a good illustration of the uses to which Theorem IV can be put. The disintegration of a single atom of radium (for instance) is accompanied by the emission of a single α particle. This process seems to take place purely by chance so that we cannot say that under given conditions a given radioactive source will emit a certain number of α particles in a given period of time. However, we can say that there is a probability distribution for each of the various possibilities (no emissions, one emission, more than one), and the hypotheses (1), (2), (3) and (4) of Sec. 75 can be advanced as reasonable assumptions in connection with these probabilities. Therefore, by Theorem IV, there is a Poisson probability distribution for the number of α particles emitted by a given source within a specified time interval.

By means of an instrument called the Geiger counter, the physicist can actually count individual α particles. If the source strength is adjusted so that the average number of α particles entering the counter in a reasonable time interval (say 10 seconds) is something easy to count (say 5 or 6), then by reading the dial on the counter at the specified intervals the experimenter can get a large number of readings on a quantity (the number of hits) which has a Poisson probability distribution. It follows that the frequency distribution for the various readings should be essentially that of the Poisson formula.

It turns out that Geiger counter experiments actually do give such results, and this can be taken as experimental evidence in favor of the assumption that the hypotheses (1), (2), (3), and (4) of Sec. 75 are applicable to the problem.

77. Two Views of the Same Problem

We have presented the problem on telephone trunk lines as a Bernoullian sequence with a Poisson approximation and that of the α particles as a strictly Poisson case following the hypotheses in Sec. 75. Actually, we can look at each of these problems in the other way.

To fit the telephone problem to hypotheses (1), (2), (3), and (4) of Sec. 75, we consider not the number of telephones in use at a given instant but the number of telephones beginning a call during a given time interval. Looked at in this way, the telephone problem seems to fit these hypotheses very well; and if we take as the time interval under consideration the average length of a call, we get essentially the same information.

To see the α particles as a Bernoullian sequence, we let a single atom represent a trial and define success as disintegration during the specified time interval. Then the assumptions that the probability of disintegration is the same for each atom and that the atoms act independently give us a Bernoullian sequence with very small p. So the answer is the same as before.

Now, one of these analyses gives the Poisson formula as an approximate answer, while the other gives it as the exact answer. This means that the two sets of hypotheses are not completely equivalent, and who is to say which set is the correct one? Experimental evidence indicates something like Poisson distributions for these and many other phenomena, but it can never be proved experimentally that the Poisson either is or is not the exact distribution in any case. The discrepancy between approximate and exact solutions is certainly within the range of experimental error and chance fluctuation in statistical data.

Essentially, it boils down to a question of which explanation we prefer, and the present-day tendency is to use something on the order of the argument in Sec. 75 whenever possible.

REFERENCES FOR FURTHER STUDY

Fry, *Probability and Its Engineering Uses*, New York (1928), Chap. VIII.

PROBLEMS

1. Let a certain volume be divided into n equal subdivisions, and suppose there are k particles distributed in this volume in such a way that for each particle the probability of being in a given subdivision is the same for all subdivisions. Suppose, further, that the probabilities for one particle are independent of the positions of the others. Show that for n and k both large and of the same order of magnitude the number of particles per subdivision has essentially a Poisson distribution.

2. Formulate a set of hypotheses modeled after those in Sec. 75 but phrased in terms of particles distributed in space as in Prob. 1.

3. Fit the problem of counting bacteria into the model of Prob. 1; into that of Prob. 2.

4. There are many examples that parallel the problem of counting bacteria almost exactly—counting white blood corpuscles, counting yeast spores in suspension, counting grit particles in lubricating oil, etc. Add some more examples to this list.

5. If a map of London is divided into equal squares and the locations of hits by "buzz bombs" during 1944 recorded on the map, show that there should be something like a Poisson distribution for the number of hits per square.

Problems 6 to 12 list a number of phenomena which might reasonably be expected to have Poisson distributions. In each case formulate the problem specifically as a sequence of Bernoullian trials and as a situation satisfying hypotheses similar to those in Sec. 75. Criticize each formulation, giving your opinion (with reasons) as to the correctness of the assumptions made.

6. The number of nuts in a chocolate almond bar.

7. The number of typographical errors per page in a newspaper.

8. The number of times per day your telephone rings.

9. The number of calls per day answered by the fire department in a large city.

10. The number of tornadoes hitting within a county in a certain number of years for the counties in the "tornado belt" of the Middle West.

11. The number of meteorites that strike the earth in a given period of time.

12. The number of twins born in a given city hospital in a given period of time.

13. Add other examples of natural phenomena that should give Poisson distributions.

14. In Prob. 6, Chap. 9, we took 1 ball from each urn and found a limiting normal distribution for the number of white balls. Suppose we take a sequence of sequences of trials consisting of 1 draw from the first urn, 2 independent draws from the second, . . . k independent draws from the kth, ... Show that as $k \to \infty$ the probability function for the number of white balls on the kth sequence tends to the Poisson probability function.

15. In statistical mechanics each "microscopic system" (atom or other fundamental unit) may be in any one of a large number of "states" (*e.g.*, energy levels). In the so-called classical statistics it is assumed that all states are equally likely and that the state of one system is independent of those of the others. Show that subject to these assumptions the number of microscopic systems in a "macroscopic system" (large collection of microscopic ones) having a given state should follow a Poisson distribution.

16. In the matching problem (see Sec. 33) we found that the probability of exactly r correspondences was

$$\frac{1}{r!} \sum_{k=0}^{n-r} \frac{(-1)^k}{k!}.$$

Show that, as $n \to \infty$, this tends to a Poisson probability function.

17. A deck of cards is shuffled; then the cards are turned up one at a time, each card being discarded after it is turned. The player calls the cards of the deck in order (AS, KS, . . . , 2S, AH, . . . , 2C), calling a card each time he turns one. Show that there is a Poisson probability distribution for the number of cards he calls correctly.

18. In the draft lottery in 1940 something like 10,000 numbers were drawn from a fishbowl one after the other. Each registrant in the draft had been assigned a registration number, and the lottery assigned him an order number determined by the position of his registration number in the sequence of drawings. Show that the Poisson distribution gives the probability that a given number of registration numbers will equal the corresponding order number.

19. Show that the probability function in Prob. 16 converges to the Poisson function so rapidly that there is virtually no distinction to be made between Probs. 17 and 18 even though the number of items being matched is 52 in one case and 10,000 in the other.

20. Find the values of the Poisson probabilities for $a = 3$ and $r = 0$, 1, 2, . . . , 10. (Use Molina's tables, if available.) Draw a graph.

21. What is the probability of 100 successes in 10,000 Bernoullian trials with $p = .01$? Hint: Use Stirling's formula. *Ans.* $.01/\sqrt{2\pi}$.

22. Find the characteristic function for the Poisson distribution.

Ans. $\exp[a(e^{it} - 1)]$.

23. Find the characteristic function for the number of successes in a single Bernoullian trial. $\qquad$ *Ans.* $q + pe^{it}$.

24. Using the results of Probs. 22 and 23, prove Theorem I by the method of characteristic functions.

25. Prove Theorem II.

26. Using hypotheses (1) and (2) Sec. 75, and considering the subdivision of the time t into equal subintervals, show that $q(t) = [q(t/n)]^n$.

27. From Prob. 26, hypothesis (3), Sec. 75, and Prob. 26, Chap. 7, show that $q(t) = e^{-at}$.

CHAPTER 11

THE LAWS OF LARGE NUMBERS

The laws of large numbers (particularly the weak law) hold in quite a wide variety of cases. We shall not attempt to give a complete description of all of these. Instead, we shall prove one or two useful theorems concerning the validity of each law and then turn to some examples.

78. Proof of the Weak Law

Many interesting cases of the weak law of large numbers can be derived from the following rather trivial lemma.

Lemma 1. If $\{y_n\}$ is a sequence of stochastic variables with

$$\lim_{n \to \infty} \text{var}(y_n) = 0,$$

then, for every fixed $\epsilon > 0$,

$$\lim_{n \to \infty} pr\{|y_n - \bar{y}_n| > \epsilon\} = 0.$$

This follows immediately from Tshebysheff's inequality (Theorem VI, Chap. 6). Let $\sigma_n^2 = \text{var}(y_n)$; then,

$$pr\{|y_n - \bar{y}_n| > t\sigma_n\} < \frac{1}{t^2}.$$

Setting $\epsilon = t\sigma_n$, we have

$$pr\{|y_n - \bar{y}_n| > \epsilon\} < \frac{\sigma_n^2}{\epsilon^2};$$

and for fixed ϵ, the right-hand side tends to zero by hypothesis.

Turning to the law of large numbers itself, let us take a sequence $\{x_k\}$ of stochastic variables and let

$$B_n = \text{var}\left(\sum_{k=1}^{n} x_k\right).$$

One of the simplest proofs of the weak law depends on the behavior of B_n and nothing more. Let us begin with that.

Theorem I.   If $B_n = o(n^2)$, the weak law of large numbers holds.

This follows immediately from Lemma 1.   For the y_n of the lemma, we use

$$M_n = \frac{1}{n} \sum_{k=1}^{n} (x_k - \bar{x}_k).$$

From (c) of Theorem IV, Chap. 6, we have

$$\text{var}(M_n) = \frac{B_n}{n^2};$$

so our present hypotheses imply those of the lemma, and the result on applying Lemma 1 is exactly the weak law of large numbers—see Definition 3, Chap. 8.

The student should note that Theorem I can be applied to dependent as well as independent variables.   In dependent cases the behavior of B_n may be difficult to determine; but if this can be done and $B_n/n^2 \to 0$, then the weak law applies.   Let us turn now to some corollaries in which conditions for the weak law are stated in terms of the individual variables x_k instead of in terms of the variance of the sum.   As usual, we shall designate $\text{var}(x_k)$ by b_k.   From Corollary 2 to Theorem VII, Chap. 6, we see that, if the variables x_k are uncorrelated by pairs, then $B_n = \Sigma b_k$.   In these cases we can give a number of useful characterizations of the conditions under which the weak law holds.

Corollary 1.   If the variables x_k are uncorrelated by pairs, each of the following conditions is sufficient for the weak law of large numbers:

(a) $\max_{k \leq n} b_k = o(n)$

(b) The variances b_k are uniformly bounded

(c) The variables x_k are uniformly bounded

(d) The variables x_k are identical and have second moments

These results all follow immediately from Theorem I.   If the variables x_k are totally independent, we can use the method of characteristic functions to show that in the case of identical variables the existence of first moments is sufficient for the weak law to hold.   (See Prob. 14 at the end of this chapter.)

79. Convergence in Probability

The weak law of large numbers involves a special case of what is known as convergence in probability. If $y_1, y_2, y_3, \ldots$ is a sequence of stochastic variables and a is a constant, we say that y_n *converges in probability* to a provided that, for each $\epsilon > 0$,

$$\lim_{n \to \infty} pr\{|y_n - a| < \epsilon\} = 1.$$

Clearly, in this terminology the weak law of large numbers says that M_n converges in probability to zero.

Convergence in probability has many of the formal properties of ordinary convergence of a sequence of numbers or functions, but these do not follow just because we have used the word "convergence." We must prove them. The student should note that each of the proofs below begins just like the proof in any calculus book of the corresponding property of ordinary convergence of sequences, but slightly different considerations are necessary to finish the proof in each case.

Theorem II. If y_n converges in probability to a and z_n converges in probability to b, then

    (a) $y_n + z_n$ converges in probability to $a + b$.
    (b) $y_n z_n$ converges in probability to ab.
    (c) y_n / z_n converges in probability to a/b provided that $b \neq 0$.

To prove (a), we note that

$$(y_n + z_n) - (a + b) = (y_n - a) + (z_n - b);$$

so

$$|(y_n + z_n) - (a + b)| \leq |y_n - a| + |z_n - b|.$$

Now, the usual argument is that if the right-hand side is small so is the left, and convergence of the sum is proved. Here, however, the question is a little more complicated. We are concerned with the probability that these differences are small, and the argument runs something like this: Because of the above inequality,

$$|(y_n + z_n) - (a + b)| \geq \epsilon$$

implies that

$$|y_n - a| \geq \frac{\epsilon}{2} \quad \text{or} \quad |z_n - b| \geq \frac{\epsilon}{2}$$

(or both). Therefore, by (d) of Theorem I, Chap. 2,

$$pr\{|(y_n + z_n) - (a + b)| \geq \epsilon\} \leq pr\left\{|y_n - a| \geq \frac{\epsilon}{2} \text{ or } |z_n - b| \geq \frac{\epsilon}{2}\right\}$$

$$\leq pr\left\{|y_n - a| \geq \frac{\epsilon}{2}\right\} + pr\left\{|z_n - b| \geq \frac{\epsilon}{2}\right\}.$$

The last inequality is obtained from (e) of Theorem I, Chap. 2. Now, each of these last two probabilities tends to zero; therefore the first one does, and the theorem is proved.

The proofs of (b) and (c) proceed along exactly the same lines once we get the necessary inequalities set up. For the products we start with the identity

$$y_n z_n - ab = (y_n - a)(z_n - b) + a(z_n - b) + b(y_n - a).$$

From this it follows that

$$|y_n z_n - ab| \leq |y_n - a||z_n - b| + |a||z_n - b| + |b||y_n - a|,$$

and again the probability that the left-hand side is larger than ϵ may be shown to be less than or equal to the sum of probabilities each of which tends to zero.

The identity we need for (c) is

$$\frac{y_n}{z_n} - \frac{a}{b} = \frac{(y_n - a)(b - z_n) + a(b - z_n)}{b^2 + b(z_n - b)} + \frac{(y_n - a)}{b}.$$

From this it follows that, for $|z_n - b| < |b|$,

$$\left|\frac{y_n}{z_n} - \frac{a}{b}\right| \leq \frac{|y_n - a||b - z_n| + |a||b - z_n|}{b^2 - |b||z_n - b|} + \frac{|y_n - a|}{|b|}.$$

The left-hand side may be too large because $|z_n - b|$ is so large in comparison with $|b|$ that the first fraction has a small denominator; or it may be too large because one of the numerators on the right is large. Each of these possibilities has probability tending to zero, and the result follows in the usual manner.

80. Applications to Sampling

The ideas in this chapter find a great number of applications in the theory of sampling. If the student wants a thorough treatment of this subject, we must refer him to a treatise on statistics. In this section we shall indicate only a few results that follow more or less easily from the theorems we have proved.

Let us recall the picture (see Sec. 64) of a sequence of independent random samples from some population. First, let us organize the terminology and notation we want to use.

The *population* has:

A distribution function $F(x)$—equal to the probability that the measurement being studied is less than or equal to x

A probability (or density) function $f(x)$

A mean $\bar{x}$

A variance σ^2

Other moments in case we need them

The *individual samples* are independent stochastic variables x_k, each having the distribution function $F(x)$ of the population. Therefore, each x_k has mean $\bar{x}$ and variance σ^2.

The *sample aggregate* is the sequence of stochastic variables x_1, x_2, x_3, . . . , x_n. In terms of these variables we define the following:

The *sample mean:* $x^* = \dfrac{1}{n} \displaystyle\sum_{k=1}^{n} x_k$.

The *sample variance:* $s^2 = \dfrac{1}{n} \displaystyle\sum_{k=1}^{n} (x_k - x^*)^2$.

The *sample distribution:* $F^*(x)$. This is $1/n$ times the number of values of k for which $x_k \leq x$.

The *sample relative frequency:* $f^*(x)$. In case the samples are discrete variables we let $f^*(x)$ be $1/n$ times the number of values of k for which $x_k = x$. In the continuous case we subdivide the range of sample values into disjoint intervals and define $f^*(x)$ at the mid-point of each of these as $1/n$ times the number of values of k for which x_k is in the subinterval.

At this point we should pause to emphasize that x^* and s^2 are stochastic variables in contrast to $\bar{x}$ and σ^2 which are (unknown) constants. Furthermore, for each x, $F^*(x)$ is a stochastic variable, and so is $f^*(x)$, while $F(x)$ and $f(x)$ are fixed functions of x.

First, let us compute a few moments:

Theorem III. $E(x^*) = \bar{x}$.

This follows immediately from the fact that $E(x_k) = \bar{x}$ for each k; so

$$E(x^*) = \frac{1}{n} \sum E(x_k) = \frac{1}{n} \cdot n\bar{x} = \bar{x}.$$

Theorem IV. $\mathrm{var}(x^*) = \dfrac{\sigma^2}{n}$

By Theorem V, Chap. 6

$$\text{var}(x^*) = \sum \text{var}\left(\frac{x_k}{n}\right)$$
$$= \frac{\Sigma\sigma^2}{n^2}$$
$$= \frac{\sigma^2}{n}.$$

Theorem V. $E(s^2) = \dfrac{(n-1)\sigma^2}{n}.$

First, we note that

$$s^2 = \frac{1}{n}\sum (x_k^2 - 2x^*x_k + x^{*2})$$
$$= \frac{1}{n}\sum x_k^2 - x^{*2}.$$

The result now follows as soon as we note that

$$E\left(\frac{1}{n}\sum x_k^2\right) = \frac{1}{n}\sum E(x_k^2) = \frac{1}{n}\sum (\sigma^2 + \bar{x}^2) = \sigma^2 + \bar{x}^2,$$

and

$$E(x^{*2}) = \text{var}(x^*) + [E(x^*)]^2 = \frac{\sigma^2}{n} + \bar{x}^2.$$

As a direct application of (d) of Corollary 1 to Theorem I we have the following:

Theorem VI. x^* converges in probability to $\bar{x}$.

From this and (b) of Theorem II it follows that x^{*2} converges in probability to $\bar{x}^2$. By applying (d) of Corollary 1 to Theorem I to the sequence $\{x_k^2\}$, we see that $\Sigma x_k^2/n$ converges in probability to $\sigma^2 + \bar{x}^2$. Combining these results by (a) of Theorem II, we have the following:

Theorem VII. s^2 converges in probability to σ^2.

It would appear from this last result that s^2 is a reasonable estimate of σ^2. It is, in the sense that for large n a single value of s^2 has a large probability of being close to σ^2. However, if we take a fixed value of n (large or small) and take a sequence of m sample aggregates, each consisting of n samples, and compute s^2 for each one, then we can apply (d) of Corollary 1 to Theorem I to the sequence of sample variances to find that as $m \to \infty$ the arithmetic mean of these converges in probability not to σ^2 but to $(n-1)\sigma^2/n$. For large n, this discrepancy is not worth worrying about, but in general we can make our estimate of σ^2 more precise (in the sense just noted) by using, instead of s^2,

$$s'^2 = \frac{ns^2}{n-1} = \frac{1}{n-1}\left[\sum x_k^2 - \frac{1}{n}\left(\sum x_k\right)^2\right].$$

To return to the discussion of sample means in Sec. 64, let us take s' as an estimate of σ. Then by the central limit theorem,

(1) $$pr\left\{|x^* - \bar{x}| \leq \alpha s'/\sqrt{n}\right\} \simeq \int_{-\alpha}^{\alpha} \frac{1}{\sqrt{2\pi}} e^{-z^2/2}\,dz.$$

A quick look at a table of the normal distribution now gives us the results most commonly associated with s':

(2) $$pr\left\{|x^* - \bar{x}| \leq \frac{.675s'}{\sqrt{n}}\right\} \simeq \frac{1}{2},$$

(3) $$pr\left\{|x^* - \bar{x}| \leq \frac{s'}{\sqrt{n}}\right\} \simeq .6826 \simeq \frac{2}{3}.$$

Finally, let us note that, for each k,

$$pr\{x_k \leq x\} = F(x);$$

so the variable $F^*(x)$ is, for each x, just the number of successes in n Bernoullian trials with $p = F(x)$. We have seen in any number of instances that for a Bernoullian sequence $E(r/n) = p$; so $E(F^*) = F$, and the weak law of large numbers applies (the Bernoullian case can be made to fit any of the conditions listed in Corollary 1 to Theorem I) to tell us as follows:

Theorem VIII. For each x, $F^*(x)$ converges in probability to $F(x)$.

In the discrete case (possible values of the samples form a discrete set) the same argument tells us that, for each x, $f^*(x)$ converges in probability to $f(x)$. In the continuous case it is a little more complicated. To have the sample relative frequency converge to the density function, we must increase the number of intervals as we increase the number of samples. A theorem of this sort can be obtained, but we shall not go into the details here.

81. Example—A Numerical Problem

By way of illustration of the ideas suggested in the last section, let us take a set of data and compute some of the quantities we have been talking about. The data in the accompanying table are just some

we made up, but they will serve as an example. We have assumed that
the problem was one in which the sample variables automatically have
integer values. Perhaps they are the count on something—*e.g.*, the
number of defective cartridges in a case or, the number of bad potatoes
in a bushel. In our table the column labeled x gives the values of the
sample variables; r is the number of samples producing the indicated
value. The sum of the r column gives us n, the total number of samples, and the next column, labeled r/n, gives what we have called the
sample relative frequency. The other columns are for convenience in
computation. Note that the sum of the rx column gives Σx_k, and the
sum of the rx^2 column gives Σx_k^2.

TABLE OF HYPOTHETICAL SAMPLE DATA

x	r	r/n	rx	rx^2
0	3	.003	0	0
1	15	.015	15	15
2	44	.044	88	176
3	89	.089	267	801
4	133	.133	532	2,128
5	160	.160	800	4,000
6	162	.162	972	5,832
7	137	.137	959	6,713
8	102	.102	816	6,528
9	69	.069	621	5,589
10	41	.041	410	4,100
11	25	.025	275	3,025
12	12	.012	144	1,728
13	5	.005	65	845
14	2	.002	28	312
15	1	.001	15	225
	1,000	1.000	6,007	42,017

From this table it appears that

$$x^* = \frac{6,007}{1,000} = 6.007,$$

$$s^2 = \frac{1}{1,000}\left[42,017 - \frac{(6,007)^2}{1,000}\right] = 5.975,$$

$$s'^2 = \frac{1}{999}\left[42,017 - \frac{(6,007)^2}{1,000}\right] = 5.980,$$

$$\frac{s'}{\sqrt{n}} = \sqrt{.00598} = 0.0806.$$

On the basis of this information we can say that the population mean $\bar{x}$ should be approximately 6. In fact, from (3), Sec. 80 it follows that, if we estimate

$$5.926 \leq \bar{x} \leq 6.088,$$

there is a probability of approximately $\tfrac{2}{3}$ that we are correct.

We should like to call special attention to the way in which we have stated the significance of (3), Sec. 80, in this problem. Through all the discussion in the preceding section we regarded x^* as the stochastic variable, not $\bar{x}$. Therefore, it would be improper to interpret (3), Sec. 80, as saying that

$$pr\{5.926 \leq \bar{x} \leq 6.088\} \simeq \tfrac{2}{3}.$$

If $\bar{x}$ has a probability distribution, we have not made any study of it; so we should not interpret our results as probabilities concerning $\bar{x}$.

Finally, it follows from Theorem VIII that for each value of x there is a reasonably large probability that the value of r/n listed in the table is close to the value of the population probability function $f(x)$.

82. The a Posteriori Approach

The weak law of large numbers applied to a Bernoullian sequence of trials gives us the information that

$$\lim_{n \to \infty} pr\left\{\left|\frac{r}{n} - p\right| < \epsilon\right\} = 1.$$

The direct physical interpretation of this is that, if p is known because of the nature of the experiment, the law of numbers gives us a prediction as to the nature of the results. It is quite natural, however, to use it the other way. Given the result of a large number of trials, we might reasonably say that the law of large numbers lends credence to the assumption that the (presumably unknown) value of p is close to r/n.

However, the direct attack on this latter problem would seem to be through Bayes' theorem—(1), Sec. 21. After all, the value of p is the hypothesis, and the experimental ratio r/n is the result; so any probability for p on the basis of a knowledge of r/n would seem to be an a posteriori probability. If we try to solve the problem in this manner, we meet with the difficulty always encountered in the use of Bayes' theorem; viz., to find the a posteriori probability of a certain hypothesis, we must have a priori probabilities for all possible hypotheses. In this particular case, we want the conditional probability that

$$\left|\frac{r}{n} - p\right| < \epsilon,$$

given that there were r successes in n trials.   To use Bayes' theorem, we need a set of a priori probabilities for all values of p between zero and one.

For the sake of getting a problem set up, let us assume that, a priori p is uniformly distributed on the unit interval.   That is, for

$$0 \le a \le b \le 1,$$
$$pr\{a \le p \le b\} = b - a.$$

There is no really convincing justification for this assumption, but it gives us something to work with.   From it we can compute the conditional probabilities,

$$pr_{r,n}\{a \le p \le b\},$$

given that there were r successes in n trials.   Not only that, but we can prove the following:

Theorem IX.   If $pr\{a \le p \le b\} = b - a$, then

$$\lim_{n \to \infty} pr_{r,n} \left\{ \left| \frac{r+1}{n+2} - p \right| < \epsilon \right\} = 1$$

for every constant $\epsilon > 0$.

Let us divide the unit interval up into k equal subdivisions.   Then the events B_i of (1), Sec. 21, are the events "p lies in the ith subdivision," which we shall approximate by $p = i/k$.   Thus

$$pr\{B_i\} = \frac{1}{k}.$$

Now, A will be the event "r successes in n trials."   So, by Theorem I, Chap. 4,

$$pr_{B_i}\{A\} = {}^nC_r \left(\frac{i}{k}\right)^r \left(1 - \frac{i}{k}\right)^{n-r}.$$

Hence, by (1), Sec. 21,

$$pr_{r,n}\{a \le p \le b\} = \frac{\sum_{\substack{i \ge ka \\ k}}^{\substack{i \le kb}} {}^nC_r \left(\frac{i}{k}\right)^r \left(1 - \frac{i}{k}\right)^{n-r} \frac{1}{k}}{\sum_{i=1}^{k} {}^nC_r \left(\frac{i}{k}\right)^r \left(1 - \frac{i}{k}\right)^{n-r} \frac{1}{k}}$$

subject to the approximations $p = i/k$ used to represent the events B_i. These approximations become more accurate as $k \to \infty$; and as this happens, the two sums above tend to definite integrals.   Therefore,

$$pr_{n,r}\{a \le p \le b\} = \frac{\int_a^b x^r(1-x)^{n-r}\,dx}{\int_0^1 x^r(1-x)^{n-r}\,dx}$$

$$= \frac{1}{B(r+1, n-r+1)} \int_a^b x^r(1-x)^{n-r}\,dx.$$

In other words, the conditional probabilities for the values of p are represented by a stochastic variable whose density function is

$$\frac{x^r(1-x)^{n-r}}{B(r+1, n-r+1)}.$$

Now (Prob. 17, Chap. 7), this variable has mean

$$\frac{r+1}{n+2}$$

and variance

$$\frac{(r+1)(n-r+1)}{(n+2)^2(n+3)}.$$

Since this latter is clearly $O(n^{-1})$, the result follows from Lemma 1.

Having manufactured a probability distribution for p, we are (in contrast to the situation in the preceding section) entitled to make statements of the form $pr\{\alpha \le p \le \beta\} = \tau$.   Before we regard this as a great forward step, however, we should take a closer look at the interpretation that is to be placed on a statement of this sort.   Stated in words, Theorem IX says something to this effect: If a number p is chosen at random between 0 and 1 and a Bernoullian sequence of experiments devised having this number as the probability of success, then, knowing that this experiment produced r successes in n trials, we can say that the chances are that the number chosen was close to r/n. It is the necessity for an a priori assumption that robs this interpretation of most of its usefulness.   Without such an assumption we cannot make direct probability statements about p, but we can say (by direct application of the weak law) that there is a large probability for the correctness of the obvious estimate $p \simeq r/n$.   This being the case, it follows from Theorem VIII that, if we consistently make estimates of this sort, there is a large probability that we shall be right most of the time.   Most authorities prefer this latter analysis of the problem.

83. Proof of the Strong Law

The necessary and sufficient condition for the strong law of large numbers to hold is as yet unknown.   The best known theorem is that of Kolmogoroff to the effect that the strong law holds provided that

$$\sum_{k=1}^{\infty} \frac{b_k}{k^2}$$

is convergent. We shall not attempt to prove this theorem here. Instead, we shall impose a much stronger hypothesis which makes the proof easier but is still satisfied in many practical cases.

Lemma 2. If a stochastic variable x has a fourth moment, it has a second moment, and $E(x^2) \leq [E(x^4)]^{1/2}$.

This follows from Schwarz's inequality (Theorem VIII, Chap. 6). We replace x by x^2 and y by 1, and Schwarz's inequality says just what we want it to.

Lemma 3. If $x_1, x_2, x_3, \ldots$ is a sequence of independent stochastic variables with $\bar{x}_k = 0$ for each k, and if the fourth moments of the x_k's are uniformly bounded, then

$$E\left[\left(\sum_{k=1}^{n} x_k\right)^4\right] = O(n^2).$$

If the fourth moments are bounded, it follows from Lemma 2 that the second moments are too. Let K be the bound on all the second and fourth moments. If we expand $(\Sigma x_k)^4$, we get terms of three types:

n terms of the form x_k^4
$3n(n-1)$ terms of the form $x_j^2 x_k^2$
Other terms in which at least one variable appears to the first power

Since each x_k has mean zero and the variables are independent, each term in our third category has expectation zero. Hence,

$$E\left[\left(\sum_{k=1}^{n} x_k\right)^4\right] = \sum_{k} E(x_k^4) + \sum_{j,k} E(x_j^2)E(x_k^2)$$
$$\leq nK + 3n(n-1)K^2$$
$$= O(n^2).$$

Theorem X. If $x_1, x_2, x_3, \ldots$ is a sequence of independent stochastic variables with uniformly bounded fourth moments, then the strong law of large numbers holds.

We apply Tshebysheff's inequality (Theorem VI, Chap. 6) to the variable M_n^2 and get

$$pr\{M_n^2 \geq t[E(M_n^4)]^{1/2}\} \leq \frac{1}{t^2}.$$

Now, we assign t so that

$$t[E(M_n^4)]^{1/2} = n^{-1/4};$$

then

$$pr\{|M_n| \geq n^{-1/8}\} \leq n^{1/2}E(M_n^4).$$

By Lemma 3,

$$E(M_n^4) = n^{-4} \cdot O(n^2) = O(n^{-2});$$

therefore

$$pr\{|M_n| \geq n^{-1/8}\} = n^{1/2} \cdot O(n^{-2}) = O(n^{-3/2}).$$

If M_n does not tend to zero, then for every k there is an $n \geq k$ for which $|M_n| \geq n^{-1/8}$. For each k, the probability of having such an $n \geq k$ is [by (e) of Theorem I, Chap. 2] less than or equal to

$$\sum_{n=k}^{\infty} pr\{|M_n| \geq n^{-1/8}\} = \sum_{n=k}^{\infty} O(n^{-3/2}).$$

Therefore, the probability that M_n does not tend to zero is less than or equal to

$$\sum_{n=k}^{\infty} O(n^{-3/2})$$

for every k. However, $\Sigma O(n^{-3/2})$ is a convergent series; so this remainder tends to zero as $k \to \infty$. Hence, the only nonnegative number less than or equal to

$$\sum_{n=k}^{\infty} O(n^{-3/2})$$

for every k is zero itself, and the theorem is proved.

If the x_k's are identical and have fourth moments, then these moments are uniformly bounded—they are all the same. We thus have the following corollary, applicable to many practical cases:

Corollary 1. If the variables x_k are independent and identical and have fourth moments, then the strong law of large numbers holds.

84. Example—Decimal Expansions

Let us say that a number has a normal decimal expansion provided that each integer $0, 1, 2, \ldots, 9$ appears, on the average, once in every

10 decimal places.   To be more specific, let r_i $(i = 0, 1, 2, \ldots , 9)$ be the number of times we find the integer i in the first n decimal places. Then, the decimal expansion is normal if, for each i,

$$\lim_{n = \infty} \frac{r_i}{n} = \frac{1}{10}.$$

The student probably considers the rational numbers the most familiar ones.   Now, a rational number has a repeating decimal expansion; so the only rational numbers with normal decimal expansions are those for which a cycle in the expansion contains each of the digits 0, 1, 2, . . . , 9 the same number of times.   The simplest of these would be

$$\frac{123456789}{9999999999} = .01234567890123456789 \cdots .$$

However, the strong law of large numbers tells us that, if a number t is chosen at random between 0 and 1, then the probability that its decimal expansion is normal is equal to unity.   To see this, we apply the strong law ten times.   For example, suppose we are interested in 7's.   Let

$$x_k = \begin{cases} 1 & \text{if the } k\text{th decimal place is a 7,} \\ 0 & \text{otherwise.} \end{cases}$$

Clearly, the variables x_k are identical and have fourth moments.   By Prob. 33, Chap. 3, they are totally independent; so Corollary 1 to Theorem X applies and tells us that

$$pr \left\{ \lim_{n \to \infty} \sum_{k=1}^{n} \frac{x_k}{n} = \frac{1}{10} \right\} = 1.$$

Now,

$$r_7 = \sum_{k=1}^{n} x_k;$$

so the result is proved as far as 7's are concerned.

The way to extend this to all 10 digits simultaneously is to consider the complementary events.   We see from the above argument that

$$pr \left\{ \lim_{n \to \infty} \frac{r_i}{n} \neq \frac{1}{10} \right\} = 0$$

for each i $(i = 0, 1, 2, \ldots , 9)$.   For different values of i, thee vents are not mutually exclusive; but by (e) of Theorem I, Chap. 2, the probability of failure for at least one i is less than or equal to the sum of 10 zeros.   Therefore, the probability of a normal decimal expansion is 1.

REFERENCES FOR FURTHER STUDY

Cramér, *Mathematical Methods of Statistics*, Chaps. 20, 25, 27.
Uspensky, *Introduction to Mathematical Probability*, Chaps. VI, X, XI.

PROBLEMS

1. Show that the strong (and therefore the weak) law of large numbers holds for a Bernoullian sequence of trials.

2. Show that the strong law of large numbers holds for *any* Poisson sequence of trials. (Compare Prob. 5, Chap. 9.)   There are thus Poisson sequences for which both laws of large numbers hold but the central limit theorem does not.

3. Show that, as the number of degrees of freedom tends to ∞, $\chi^2/n \to 1$ with probability 1.   Hint: Show that Corollary 1 to Theorem X applies to Prob. 10, Chap. 8.

4. Apply Tshebysheff's inequality (Theorem VI, Chap. 6) to a Bernoullian sequence of trials to get an estimate of

$$pr\left\{\left|\frac{r}{n} - p\right| < \epsilon\right\}.$$

Ans.   This probability is greater than $1 - (pq/n\epsilon^2)$.

5. Show that, for $x > 0$,

$$\int_x^\infty e^{-z^2/2}\,dz < \frac{1}{x}\,e^{-x^2/2}.$$

Hint:

$$x\int_x^\infty e^{-z^2/2}\,dz < \int_x^\infty z e^{-z^2/2}\,dz,$$

and this last expression can be integrated to give the result.

6. Apply Prob. 5 to the estimate (1), Sec. 80, for the case of Bernoullian trials to show that, for large n,

$$pr\left\{\left|\frac{r}{n} - p\right| > \epsilon\right\} < \frac{2\sqrt{pq}}{\epsilon\sqrt{n}}\,e^{-\epsilon^2 n/2pq}.$$

7. Compare Probs. 4 and 6.   Note that

$$x^{-\frac{1}{2}}e^{-x} = o(x^{-1})$$

as $x \to \infty$.   (Prove this by Lhopital's rule.)   Therefore, for large n

the central limit theorem gives a closer estimate than Tshebysheff's inequality.

8. Let $x_1, x_2, \ldots, x_n$ be independent random samples from some population. Let α_m be the mth moment of the population about zero, and let

$$a_m = \frac{1}{n} \sum_{k=1}^{n} x_k^m.$$

Assuming that α_m exists for every m, show that a_m converges in probability to α_m.

9. Using Theorem II, show that any polynomial $P(a_1, a_2, \ldots, a_m)$ in the sample moments (see Prob. 8) converges in probability to the corresponding combination of the population moments.

10. Extend Prob. 9 to rational functions of the sample moments, subject to the provision that the denominator is different from zero when the population moments are substituted.

11. Let $x_1, x_2, \ldots, x_n$ and $y_1, y_2, \ldots, y_n$ be independent sample measurements of 2 different quantities from the same population. (For example, x might be the height of a child, y his weight.) Show that the sample correlation coefficient

$$\frac{\sum_{j,k} (x_j - x^*)(y_k - y^*)}{[(\Sigma(x_k - x^*)^2)(\Sigma(y_k - y^*)^2)]^{\frac{1}{2}}}$$

converges in probability to the population correlation coefficient for these 2 quantities.

12. Find the characteristic function for the distribution in which $pr\{x = a\} = 1$, $pr\{x \neq a\} = 0$. *Ans.* e^{ita}.

13. Show that, if x has a finite first moment, the characteristic function for x may be written $\varphi(t) = 1 + it\bar{x} + o(t)$.

14. Using Probs. 12 and 13, prove Khintchine's theorem: If the variables $x_1, x_2, x_3, \ldots$ are independent and identical and have finite first moments, then the weak law of large numbers holds.

15. Show that to prove Theorem VII by means of (d) of Corollary 1 to Theorem I we must assume that the population has a fourth moment, while the same result can be obtained with no more than second moments by using Prob. 14.

16. Show that the a posteriori probabilities of Theorem IX are equal to certain a priori Bernoullian probabilities. Specifically, the conditional probability (given r successes in n trials) that $p \leq (r/n) - \epsilon$ is equal to the probability of at least $r + 1$ successes in $n + 1$ Bernoullian trials with probability of success $(r/n) - \epsilon$ on each trial. Hint: See Prob. 25, Chap. 4, and Prob. 11, Chap. 7.

17. Using Prob. 16 and applying the weak law of large numbers to the auxiliary Bernoullian sequence, give another proof of Theorem IX.

18. Show that, if x is chosen at random between $-\pi$ and π, then, given $\epsilon > 0$,

$$pr\left\{\left|\frac{1}{n}\sum_{k=1}^{n}\sin kx\right| < \epsilon\right\} \to 1$$

as $n \to \infty$. Hint: Note Prob. 33, Chap. 6, and apply (b) of Corollary 1 to Theorem I.

19. Let the functions $x_k(t)$ be defined on the unit interval $0 \le t < 1$ as follows:

$$x_k(t) = \begin{cases} 1 & \text{for } \dfrac{2i-2}{2^k} \le t < \dfrac{2i-1}{2^k} \\ -1 & \text{for } \dfrac{2i-1}{2^k} \le t < \dfrac{2i}{2^k} \end{cases}$$

$(i = 1, 2, \ldots, 2^{k-1})$. Draw the first three $x_k(t)$'s.

20. Show that, if t is chosen at random between 0 and 1, the stochastic variables $x_k(t)$ of Prob. 19 are independent.

21. Show that, if t is chosen at random between 0 and 1,

$$pr\left\{\frac{1}{n}\sum_{k=1}^{n}x_k(t) \to 0\right\} = 1.$$

22. Let t be chosen at random between 0 and 1, and let $m_n(t)$ be the arithmetic mean of the first n digits in the decimal expansion of t. Show that $pr\{m_n(t) \to 4.5\} = 1$.

23. Generalize the example on decimal expansions at the end of this chapter. Consider dyadic expansions (see Chap. 8) and, in general, expansions in powers of $1/N$ where N is any positive integer. Show that each of these expansions has the normality property with probability 1.

24. A normal number is one which has the normality property for *every* expansion of the type suggested in Prob. 23. Show that with probability 1 a number chosen at random is normal. Hint: Show that the probability of failure here is less than or equal to the sum of an infinite sequence of zeros.

INDEX